GARDEN HOPPING

A MEMOIR OF ADOPTION

JONATHAN RENDALL

CANONGATE

Edinburgh · New York · Melbourne

GARDEN HOPPING

First published in Great Britain in 2006 by
Canongate Books Ltd, 14 High Street,
Edinburgh EH1 1TE

1

Copyright © Jonathan Rendall, 2006

The moral right of the author has been asserted

British Library Cataloguing-in-Publication Data
A catalogue record for this book is available on
request from the British Library

1 84195 596 5 (10-digit ISBN)
978 1 84195 596 4 (13-digit ISBN)

Typeset by
Palimpsest Book Production Ltd,
Polmont, Stirlingshire
Printed and bound in Germany by GGP Media GmbH, Poessneck

www.canongate.net

Contents

For Andrew and Kate

Acknowledgements

For their invaluable support and advice during the writing of this book I would like to thank my agent, Stan, and all involved at Canongate Books, in particular my editor, Helen Bleck.

Prologue
Dreamworld

We went up the steep hill of Hangman's Lane on our bikes, me and George, my son. He was eight. It was a hot summer's day. The rape shimmered in the hot air, in the fields on either side of the narrow lane.

I tracked him up the hill. He was a good boy. All fathers say the same but objectively he was. Everyone said that.

Each Sunday we aped the stars of the Tour de France cycle race. He was Richard Virenque, the French climber. I was Indurain, five-times Tour winner.

We paused at the top, by the entrance to the wood. 'Another victory in the Alps for Virenque then, Dad,' he said.

'Don't get cocky, sunshine,' I said. 'It's not over yet.'

We turned the bikes round and sped back down, the air whistling. I could see the white face of our house down below, beyond the overgrown Leylandii trees.

She would be in the garden. My daughters would be behind her on the grass, playing. They were younger than George. And soon I would be leaving them all . . .

Not now. Maybe not next year. But I would. I knew I would . . .

No, I wouldn't be leaving them. I'd just be leaving her. It wasn't that I hated her. We had given it a good go. We met at nineteen.

My God . . .

I realised that in years to come I would remember this view of the white face of the house, from this bike on this ancient hill, and that the memory would reintrude as a golden time.

So it was ludicrous, you see? The whole thing.

I remembered the race and sped up to try and catch him. He was too far ahead. I can never catch him on the run-in. There's too much gravel on the road.

We skidded to a halt and he said: 'And Virenque takes a commanding overall lead.'

We bunged the bikes into the old garage and walked in. George ran out of the back door to join the others. I went into the kitchen. I was cooking a roast. After lunch we would do the running races around the copse in the middle of the garden. My youngest girl, Xanthe, was improving rapidly. I'd have to adapt her handicap mark.

I looked out of the window at them and at the tangled summer green. I imagined a future time when I would come to visit them, at another house. Well, she wouldn't want to stay in this one after I'd gone. I knew she didn't like it here. I loved it. They loved it. No, the children I would never leave. Where would the new house be? London? Oxford, maybe? Yes, she had always liked the idea of living in Oxford.

And on the way out, after visiting them, I'd just leave a poem for her on the sideboard. For some reason I imagined it written in someone else's lipstick. Some as-yet-unidentified person. It would read:

The bridge, the stream,
The scurrying waters
My shy son, my lovely daughters

3

Garden Hopping

All gone, like a dream
Not even true
But in the end
It was you
It was you

1
Something To Do

I needed something to do. I had been a boxing writer, a boxing manager, a general journalist, a novelist. Career-wise I had hit a dead end. I knew these things came in cycles but I was fed up with waiting. The previous day I had had a win on the horses and spent it on a green racing bike. I was, if anything, a runner not a cyclist. I'd gambled £12,000 for a publisher and was soon to gamble another £12,000 for a TV company. I don't know why I'd agreed to either because I knew I'd never make any money out of it. I don't even like gambling.

All right, I do.

I was living on a fly-blown Suffolk pig farm. You couldn't even open the windows. I was thirty-four years old and skint. I got up from my desk, looked at myself in the mirror and said out loud: 'What the *fuck* are you doing?'

My only friend nearby was Marek. He was a highly amusing man of Polish extraction. He consciously confused the words 'sexist' and 'sexy', as in: 'Jesus, she was sexist.' He lived in Norfolk. That's what I'd do: cycle to Marek's on the new bike, an epic ride, and while I was doing it I'd work out what to do.

I couldn't work out anything. It was forty miles of agony. After one mile I hated that fucking bike. But I had nothing else to do so I kept on and eventually I got there, rather triumphantly I have to admit.

That night I got drunk with Marek. I was expecting him to drive me and the bike back the next morning but he said he had a business meeting. The absolute bastard. But there was no point in arguing so I just got on the bike. It seemed to me that I pulled every muscle in my body but I got back again. I still hadn't worked anything out.

I had a shower, put on a robe, put my feet up on the desk and cracked open a beer. I recalled that I had been adopted. Of course! That was it! Well, she'd given me away so the least she could do was let me get something out of it.

I walked across the fields to the village pub, the White Horse. The landlord there was a marvellous man. John, a Scottish dandy. Yellow trousers, striped shirts. He was a terrible hypochondriac, but that was part of his charm. His daughter had died young – a Jimi Hendrix job. Now he was on his own.

The only people who went in there were me, a guy who sold birdseed and a young incipient alcoholic who claimed to be a tree-cutter. All of us apart from Birdseed were phonetically called 'John'.

John the landlord greeted me in the usual manner. What I liked about him at base was that he was always pleased to see me.

'Ah, Johnny!' he said as I walked in, closing the latch carefully behind me, as it could swing open in the wind. 'Have you anything in the papers today?'

No, I averred. I got my pint and stood by the bar, said hello to Birdseed and tree-cutter John, and told John the landlord what I'd decided to do. Adoption, finding my mother, etc.

'Don't do it,' John said.

'What?' I said.

'I knew a guy once who was adopted,' John

went on. 'Very successful he was. He was high up in the BBC. But he was obsessed with finding his real mother. Finally he found her. He was in his forties by then. And she was a real council-estate job. He moved her out of there. He gave up everything for her so they could be together. His job, his old home, everything. And then when his money ran out, so did she. It destroyed him. Terrible.'

Christ, thanks for that, John. Have a nice day yourself. I laughed. This BBC bloke sounded like a complete idiot. How could you go all-in like that after forty years of not knowing someone? I was not obsessed. I was just curious. It was no big deal. I would not go all-in.

I bought a round of drinks and Birdseed chipped in that his mum was a right old slag who he hadn't talked to for ten years. There. You see this sentimentality is misplaced. Curiosity. My adopted mother once gave me a letter all about my real one and within a week I had lost it. I can't even have been all that curious.

Oh cut the caustic will you. It doesn't work and it didn't for Birdseed either. You saw the way his eyes changed when he said that. He was trying to impress you but he regretted it. Losing that

*letter killed you. Don't you remember how much
you've thought about it. Every week of your
conscious existence you've wondered what she'd
look like and what it would be like for her to put
her hand on your hair.*

For Christ's sake, I'm thirty-four. I don't need a
mother. I've been all right without one. I fell out
with my adopted one years and years ago.

I left the pub and got on the green bike. I
cycled through the lightless Suffolk fields, the thin
trees brushing past. God I like that countryside.
It's my home. I don't know why.

The next week I went to Oxford, where I was
born, and a woman from Social Services who
looked just like Dawn French told me I'd been put
in care after thirty-eight days. She gave me some
names and told me my mother had come from
Devon. He had denied paternity, but I wasn't
really interested in him. For weeks I followed a
trail through library phonebooks.

Then I found one, a Marianne Smith who
had moved from Devon to a council estate by
Wormwood Scrubs. I rang her. When I explained
she dropped the phone and left it hanging there.
So, it must be her.

I was going to go down. I was thinking of ways to save her. But it didn't feel right. You have to check these things out. After two more calls I hit the jackpot. So it was not Wormwood Scrubs.

Simon. My half-brother, it turned out. He lived in Bristol. He was two years younger than me. He had another brother who was in the army. Tom. He'd gone in at sixteen. I suppose I would have done too. She still lived in Devon. Simon sounded like a nice bloke. He said: 'Mum's been waiting for this call for a long time.'

Christ. Well I was in it now. Something to do.

2
World Stair-Jumping Record

The story really starts nearly three decades earlier.

My brother Andrew could not have been more different from me. He was two years younger. He was blond and wore thick glasses. He hated sport and liked girls' things. For one of his birthdays he asked for a toy Hoover. At school they asked me about it. 'Is he really your brother?' I wanted a younger brother who was in the teams, like me. Once I made Andrew take the cricket bat and then bowled as fast as possible at him. Bouncers.

Andrew clung to Mum and Dad, putting his hands round them and kissing them. They would never let me do that. It was because he'd say he was ill.

Kate was more like me, even though I remembered us collecting her from a different family when she was a baby. She was good at ballet and gymnastics. Mum liked ballet. There was a portrait of Margot Fonteyn hanging by the stairs.

Sometimes Kate and I ganged up on Andrew, although we always made it up. Whatever our differences, I knew that we were together and that I was their leader.

At about the age of eight, I found the adoption certificate in the back of the desk. I was once called Ben Smith, and my mother's name was Marianne. I was excited. Two mothers! Mum was out shopping. I went to the kitchen cupboard where the local directories were. She must be around here somewhere. There were loads of Smiths, but I would find her. I went out on my bike, but the people didn't seem the right age, so I went back for more addresses.

Mum walked into the kitchen while I was looking. I told her what I was doing. She was furious. She started to cry. She didn't talk to me for a while. They told Andrew and Kate that we were all three of us adopted, after that.

At around that time I was trying to break my world record at stair-jumping. For the attempt I roped in Andrew and Kate. They had to sit at the bottom of the stairs for me to vault over. They were sitting there, with their knees together. It was going to be a difficult manoeuvre, because the stairs were L-shaped. I had never tried it from the very top before. I would have to leap forward, palm off the wall by Margot Fonteyn and then come over Andrew and Kate at a narrow trajectory.

I leapt off, the palm-off went well, I was over Andrew and Kate but . . . too high. My head hit the ceiling. I semi-knocked myself out and it seemed to me that I had broken my arm. I had, in fact.

I came round and Mum was standing over me. 'You stupid child,' she said.

Now I didn't let her kiss me good night any more. I ran away but only reached the end of the road before she caught me.

Mum took me on all these outings and courses: acting, English-speaking, museums, country houses. I traipsed around with her, watching her, seeing what mood she was in and how I should act.

She gave me things, so many things they embarrassed me. At Harvest Festival the basket I brought into school was three times the size of anyone else's. 'You ungrateful boy.'

At the diving course at the leisure centre the female instructor was trying to teach me a backward dive. We were both standing on the end of the springboard. I almost pulled the instructor in, fully clothed. Mum was watching from behind the glass of the café. She didn't seem to notice. What's the use of a backward dive, anyway?

3
'The Day Before', by Jonathan Rendall
(aged ten, 1974)
Excerpts from a Memoir

I was born in Nuffield Maternity Home, on the 11th of June, 1964. When I was four years old I went to a playgroup in Epsom, at St Martin's Church. Philip Vile went there as well. Then I went to Ryebrook School, Ashtead. I stayed there until I was seven years old. One thing I remember particularly about Ryebrook is that each day, after lunch, we used to have a rest hour. If we behaved badly, we had to lie on a rug (where I usually was), if we behaved a bit better, we had to sit on the green blocks, if we behaved very well, we used to sit on a chair, which was then my ambition.

* * *

Garden Hopping

MY MOST EXCITING DAY

One of my favourite pastimes is going for long cycle rides, and I will always remember the day I cycled up to Boxhill with my friend Philip Vile.

'Let's go to Boxhill,' I suggested.

'Well, I suppose that's something, yes, come on!' Said Chris.

It was alright to Say, 'Let's go to Boxhill' but from Headly to Boxhill was quite some distance, but after a long and strenuous journey, we reached our destination. After turning into a bridle path we came to the River Mole. (I almost lost my bike while carrying it over some stepping stones, however, Chris came to my aid.)

Although we were near Boxhill we wanted to reach an isolated spot where no one could See us. To reach this spot we had to wade across the river once more. This caused a problem to the other two, (Julian and Chris) but for Philip and I it was a simple job, because we had short trousers on. On reaching the other side, we were content in climbing the wooded side of the hill, and having Burr fights.

Afterwards, our ambition (after extracting the Burrs from our hair) was to build a dam across the river, which we succeeded in doing. (After falling to the stony bottom of the murky water once each.) Then we broke down a chunk of the dam. So that the water would run down it, this it did, but with so much force that it washed us all, except Julian off our feet.

I felt so embarrassed when I staggered up out of the water, bruised all over, freezing cold and wet through – while Julian was laughing his head off. In fact we felt so humiliated that we each picked up a stone and chucked it at him – that soon silenced him.

The best thing to do to raise people's spirits is to light a fire – so Chris and I climbed up the hill, collecting sticks and throwing them down to Phil and Julian below.

Once the fire got going we virtually stripped off, and held our sodden clothes slightly above the flames. After this we kicked the fire into the river – we started to wade across the river – we should have known, for they splashed us (Philip and I) with stones, which wet us through once more.

Then we unpadlocked our bikes and set off homeward.

I don't know why, but although I was soaked to the skin and numb with cold by the time I reached home in Ashtead, I felt very satisfied with the exciting day I had just lived.

* * *

Garden Hopping

AMBITIONS

When I grow up, I want to do lots of things:

Play cricket for England; Pilot a Lancaster; be a professional boxer; be a ball-boy at Wimbledon; and write a book.

4
Catteries

In her twenties and thirties Mum was a striking, dark-haired woman. I knew that from photographs. Sometimes, quite occasionally, she still dressed up in a fur coat and put perfume on. I loved it when she did that. But though Dad tried to find her places to go out to, she never liked them. She didn't like the area. She said the places were no good. I used to watch from the top of the stairs when they came back and she would tell him that crossly.

She had once worked for Alitalia. She spoke fluent Italian. She had an English girlfriend called Toni who Mum said had a much worse accent than hers. When she'd first got me she'd gone back to Italy and there'd been a terrible kerfuffle at Naples airport. I think the police might even have been involved. I had gone off down a corridor in my baby-walker without her noticing and then when she found me she lost her temper. She and Dad and Auntie Pat used to talk about it years later. I didn't remember that but I still always had to watch Mum's moods. At breakfast once she started talking to herself about not having children. She repeated it over and over.

I didn't know what she meant. I loved her. I just wanted her to love me. She didn't seem to. She was cross so often. She hit me and sometimes kicked me, but that was no big deal. Each day she gave me a clean folded handkerchief to take to school. That should mean she loved me. They always smelled so nice, of her. Sometimes I took them out just to smell them.

Mum liked Siamese cats and Standard Poodles. I went to the catteries and kennels with her to get them. She named them after people to do with musicals. The first two cats were called Gilbert and Sullivan.

I didn't remember getting Andrew, but I remembered getting Kate. I went with Mum and Dad and Andrew on a drive to a housing estate. The houses were much smaller than ours. There was a foster mother there. That's what Mum called her. The foster mother looked tired and blank. She wasn't wearing make-up like Mum. She was surrounded by children. There must have been seven or eight there. They got Kate out.

5
Christmas Day 1974

I woke up with a new strategy. Why open all your presents as soon as you can? No. This time you would leave them. Leave them for as long as was humanly possible. Leave them until it was unbearable not to open them. Just think what it would be like when you finally did . . . ? Yes.

I went into my usual Christmas Day routine. I got a ball of wool from Mum's sewing cupboard and wove it into a football. I went into the hall. I only used the hall on special occasions. It was Wembley. I breathed in the smell of the turkey cooking. Oh, it was so good.

Andrew and Kate had already opened most of their presents. Mine were still untouched. I was holding out. That was going to be so good, too.

To hold out a little longer, I went up to my room. There was a ledge outside the window that I could stand on. I stood there watching the birds. Up there it was almost as if you were one of them. This was going to be the best Christmas ever. Next I would go down and open the presents. I had held out long enough.

I heard Mum's footsteps coming along the corridor. Just from the sound of them I could tell she was furious. She came in and said: 'You ungrateful child!' She slapped me and kicked me. It wasn't too bad. She always held back that little bit. It wasn't as bad as with a boy I knew called James. I saw his mum give him a terrible kicking. Mind you, James was a real pain. I watched her doing it. I was lying flat down at the top of the stairs so they couldn't see me, looking down at them.

I lay there on the carpet in my room for a while, imagining what was going on down-stairs. They would be about to have Christmas lunch. Then I got up and started hitting a box-ing ball Mum and Dad had given me before. It was on a spring. I hit it and hit it. I was crying and crying while I did it. I'd never cried so much. Then I lay on the carpet and heard

Mum's footsteps coming again. They were softer this time.

She came in and I rested against her apron. It smelled of flour. She said: 'We love you really, you know.'

6
The First Walk

We were in the Winnebago on holiday in Canada, Dad and Mum in front, Andrew, Kate and me lying on their double bed in the top section, from where you could look out of the back window. I was eleven. It was summer and very hot, and we were just wearing T-shirts and shorts. I was wearing my 'Pepsi Lipsmackin' . . .' T-shirt again. The words went all down the front. It was my favourite one. The previous day in an ice-cream parlour when I'd wandered off, an old man had come up to me and asked me friendlily if I could recite them all without looking. He put his hand on my shoulder when I started doing it – it wasn't exactly difficult. Then Mum saw me and came running over, dived between us and pulled me away with both hands. 'Don't ever speak to strange men again,' she said crossly. I didn't know what she was on about. The man wasn't trying to hurt me. It was fun.

Dad slowly drove the Winnebago out of the grove of trees where the campsite was, and I could tell Mum was revving up as usual to tell him, For God's sake, get a move on, John. We were going to a lake to swim.

It wasn't long before we started squabbling and Mum started screaming at us, and at Dad. But we kept on and soon the squabbles broke into fights between me and Andrew, which I always won because I was much bigger than him.

The only things you had to watch with Andrew were when he told Mum I'd done things to him when I hadn't, which he'd always done quite a lot, and when he really lost his temper. Then he would go all quiet and, back at home, would walk away silently and then reappear a few minutes later at my bedroom door with a weapon in his hand. Usually it was the poker from the fireplace downstairs, or sometimes a Tonka toy. I thought Andrew could actually murder me when he had that look in his eye and I was always very careful as I got the weapon off him.

However, on this holiday for the first time Kate had started ganging up with Andrew a bit. There were even more squabbles than usual because I wanted Kate back on my side like she'd always been before.

I was pinning Andrew down and Kate said, 'Adopted boy,' under her breath. That was what Andrew said when he really wanted to enrage me, but Kate had never said it before.

I got off Andrew and they started chanting it: 'Adopted boy, adopted boy, adopted boy . . .'

I started crying. I felt my Pepsi Lipsmackin' T-shirt. It was soaked from all my sweat and my tears. I curled up on the bed and they went silent. They had never seen me like that before. I wasn't acting like their leader.

It wasn't really what they were saying, especially as they were adopted too, but the heat and thinking how nasty I'd been to Andrew for a lot of his life, and now I was starting to be nasty to Kate, too.

Eventually Kate shouted to Mum, 'Something's happened to Jonathan!'

'What? What has?' Mum said in her worried voice. She told Dad to stop the Winnebago.

She opened the back door and we all came

out on to the road. We were in a town by the lake. All around us were green lawns with sprinklers on them.

I sprinted across one of them and heard Mum and Kate's voices calling after me to stop. I kept going and when I next looked back Dad was turning the car round. But none of them could see me while he was doing it so I darted back and sprinted over another lawn.

I kept going fast. I ran over another road and found myself at the entrance to a golf club. There was a huge banner outside it announcing an international tournament and I wondered whether Peter Oosterhuis was playing in it.

I stopped running. I knew I had lost the Winnebago. It was nice walking over the putting greens with the sprinklers cooling you down.

I walked back to the campsite. It was the longest walk I'd ever done. It took me hours. Some people stopped to offer me a lift but they were all strange men and I didn't want to get in more trouble with Mum than I was already in.

As I walked down the hill to the grove, I saw they were back and that Andrew and Kate were putting out the things for our tea on the portable

table. I ate my tea off our plastic plates from the picnic basket.

Afterwards I took the football out and carried on with the tournament I'd been doing. Andrew didn't play so I played against myself. Dad came over and did a few shots. At the end Dad said, 'You shouldn't do that, son.'

'What?' I said.

'Run away like that,' Dad said.

'I didn't run away,' I said. 'I ran home.'

Dad said, 'It upsets your mother.'

Dad had his pained expression on, and I knew that Mum had asked him to come and have a word with me. Dad had been much happier just doing shots.

'And I tell you what, kiddo,' Dad added. 'I looked at the milometer and that was a ten-mile walk you did. Ten miles! That's a hell of a walk.'

'Sorry, Dad,' I said.

Dad said that was all right but that I should apologise to Mum, too. I did, and then she said what would be helpful would be if I took Andrew and Kate for a walk. They hadn't run their energy off because they'd been stuck in the car looking for me.

I got them out of the Winnebago and we

went off towards the wood that lay on a steep slope below the plateau of the campsite. On the way I noticed that on the rubbish bins there were signs saying, 'Beware of the Bears'.

Kate and Andrew were all excited and started running about wildly when we went into the wood. Then Kate fell down one of the muddy slopes and I had to go down and rescue her, while Andrew lay on the top of the slope. He was crying because of what had happened to Kate.

I shouted that there was a bear coming up towards us, a brown bear. They started scrabbling up. I grabbed Kate and then Andrew by the arms and they leant on me before running off out of the wood.

For years and years, in all sorts of different places, they would tell the story of how I saved them from the bear. But I hadn't, because there wasn't one.

7
Auntie Pat

Mum was nanny to Auntie Pat's children in America. She wasn't really my aunt. Mum looked after her four or five kids. She left London University to do it. This was before we were around. They were a military family. Pat's husband was called Stan. General Stanley Adams III. He and Pat loved each other as far as I could tell. Mum and Dad didn't seem to, really, or maybe just not in the same way. They stayed with us in Ashtead, Surrey, and Pat went out shopping for some shoes for him. They were white with tan fringes. It was around Christmas. Pat and Stan were older than Mum and Dad. They must have been in their sixties. When Stan saw the shoes he said: 'I can't wear them. They're nigger shoes.' Stan was a kind man to us. I think it was just his upbringing. He was brought up in the South.

Pat was a striking-looking woman. She had blonde hair down to her waist. Generally she wore it in plaits. She was very strong. She had won horse-races in Karachi. For a while there was a picture of her winning one on the top of Mum's chest of drawers. She talked about men liking her. Then Stan said: 'All right, Pat, all right.' They lived in Hawaii. Later we went over there. We had tans throughout the school term. I wanted to be a boxer. Pat latched on to this and took to sparring with me. She used to hit me right in the face, dancing around me. I didn't feel I could hit her back. She hit hard as well. She said I should be careful about going around throwing punches in the air. She said: 'There are Samoans here who weigh 200lb at your age and they'll beat the crap out of you.'

She came on holiday to Portugal with us. For some reason I had taken to ringing people's door-bells and running off. Pat caught me and yanked my willy hard. She did it quite frequently after that. She said: 'That's what I do to naughty boys like you.' I didn't like it, but after that I fantasised about having sex with her. I watched her sun-bathing on the roof in Portugal. She never knew I was watching. I could see her pubic hairs.

Pat had a broad American accent but insisted she was English. She had lived in England as a small girl. She said the main things she missed were wine gums.

One of her daughters, Candy, came over and stayed with us in Ashtead. She was a drug addict. She was one of the original hippies. I thought she was the most beautiful creature I had seen. She was tall and blonde and sort of drifted about. She hung out in Ashtead grave-yard with some other drug addicts. I was amazed there were any. I was honoured that drug-addict hippies existed in Ashtead.

I realised that Mum modelled herself on Pat. Pat believed in hitting children and that was why Mum did it. For Mum, her experiences in bringing up Pat's kids in 1950s' America were her own golden era. We were an extension of Pat's kids. When later we moved to Greece, Mum still bought great big bottles of Coke and Seven-Up. In Hawaii I noticed that Pat did that. It all came from Pat.

8
Clive

When I was thirteen and fourteen, if you're talking about doing things, this is what I liked doing: garden-hopping.

Clive first took me garden-hopping. He was not a 'Clive' at all. He was a right hard nut. He smoked Rothmans and went to the youth-club disco. He wore wide collars and ten-hole DMs. He had fights all the time. He advised me on them: 'If you go down, curl up.' Once he asked me to referee a fight against a boy called Ramsi, but they just swore at each other and then shook hands.

It's amazing, garden-hopping, in the dead of night. Sometimes people come out, usually the men, shaking their fists. But by then you're long gone. You're already two gardens along. You can cover whole areas, hundreds of houses.

The air goes right through you. You're like a phantom.

* * *

The first girl I went out with was called Nikki. Nikki Morecambe. Clive and people called her 'Eric', which I didn't like. She was adopted too. With her it was her father she was wary of. They lived in a big house but she kept to a little room downstairs. She said she was not trusted anywhere else. I held her hand on the road, the first hand I had held. I took her to a party. It was supposed to be soft drinks but people were smuggling in cider. A boy called Adam came up and said, 'She's nice.' And I said, 'Yeah, and she's mine.'

There was another adopted one I knew. She was an Asian girl adopted by a white couple. They lived by a river. They had children of their own. They sent their own children to private schools and her to the comprehensive.

9
The Bus

Then I was living in Greece. Dad went there to
sell Mills & Boon romances. I liked talking
to him about the internal politics of the company. It was always going on and Dad had to
watch out. We lived in an isolated area at the
foot of a mountain outside Athens. Andrew and
I lived downstairs. We weren't supposed to. Mr
Papachristou, the landlord, had only let out the
top half. Mr Papachristou had a wine cellar and
I used to take swigs before school. Then a boy
called Kalahanis said one morning: 'Hey, have
you been drinking?' I said: 'Are you joking?' I
stopped drinking before school after that. It was
too risky.

We were all sent to English boarding schools
for a while, but first Kate got expelled for drugs.
Then I got expelled for general bad behaviour.

Now Kate had dyed her hair pink. I was on speed. You could buy them over the counter as diet pills, but they were amphetamines. Mum found the pills and went ballistic. She thought I'd introduced Kate to it. I hadn't.

My friend was Jeremy. He wasn't really a 'Jeremy' either. He was older than me. He was one of the original punks. Everyone says they were, but he really was. On my sixteenth birthday I went to England on a cheap ticket with Bulgarian airways. I didn't intend to come back. I worked as a kitchen porter and a cleaner at the Department of Employment. Later I got Jeremy a job there.

He had an older sister, Nicola. She had a beautiful face but was a bit nutty. She put a tent up in her flat. She snogged me in there, but Jeremy didn't know.

I went to Somerset House, for my birth certificate, but I couldn't find it. I couldn't find her. Marianne Smith. There was a register but she wasn't on it.

I went back to Greece with the Magic Bus company. It was the bus all the hippies used. I decided to start trying at school. I stopped taking speed and raiding Mr Papachristou's cellar. One of the teachers, Rob, said he thought I was Oxbridge material. I started going down to the British Council to read the *English Historical Review*. It was edited by Angus MacIntyre of Magdalen College, Oxford. That was where I'd go.

Coming back from the British Council the bus went into a ditch. It smashed right into it. Some old crones were wailing. We were stuck there for hours. When I got back Mum and Dad didn't believe me. They thought I'd been doing something else. I told Mum about what Rob had said and she said, 'Pah.'

10
Letters to Marianne Smith

White House Farm
October 12, 1999

Dear Marianne,

As you probably noticed on the phone, I have been rendered virtually speechless by all this. If not speechless then incomprehensible. I do feel very happy, though, and relieved, because you've been so generous about my sudden re-entry to your world.

I think you're right in saying that the best thing would be to get the preliminaries over with and get back to behaving normally again (whatever that means). I have to go abroad to do some journalism work next week but am back the week starting October 25. If that's not convenient, another week would be fine. Despite what I said, weekends are as good for me as weekdays. I could come down to you or you could come up here. Perhaps I should come to Devon. I am just anxious to avoid the impression of somehow barging in and thereby upsetting people.

Anyway, whichever you'd prefer. You decide and specify, and I'll go along with it. That's how it works between mothers and sons isn't it?

I'm enclosing some photos and also a letter I wrote to you a couple of months ago. I thought about editing it or binning it in light of having found you but then thought I might as well send it as it is.

Hope to hear from you soon,
Yours,
Jonathan Rendall
[enclosure]

* * *

Dear Marianne,
Last month I finally went to Oxford Social Services to find out about my real parents. A counsellor there confirmed you were my mother. I knew a few details before. About ten years ago I was given sight of a letter but I was not able to

keep it. It's possible I lost it but I don't think I would have done. Certainly I only saw it the once. The subject of my adoption was not something that was brought up by my adopted parents and, knowing their uneasiness, I didn't bring it up either.

I have certainly thought about it a lot – who you were, what you were/are doing at particular points in time, what you look like – though I know this might sound strange given that it has taken me thirty-five years to make that trip to Oxford. I don't know exactly why I didn't before. I made steps to do so several times from the age of about sixteen and even earlier, but mainly I just thought about it. Also, organisation-wise I am terrible. I want to stress that I would completely understand if you just wanted to forget. I wouldn't be hurt, and I wouldn't press to meet you unless you really wanted to, though it would be nice. Anyway, I thought perhaps you might like some information about what became of me.

Two things in particular struck me during the meeting with the counsellor. One was how many times you had to move house. Coupled with the breech birth, it sounded like I brought you a serial *dose of discomfort. I hope that subsequently you recovered from it all and have been happy. The other thing was that Brian Phillips is termed merely as my 'putative' father. I took this to mean either he didn't know about the birth or denied paternity.*

As you probably know, my adopted parents became John and Jay Rendall. I was brought up mostly in Ashtead, Surrey. When I was fourteen my father made the rather startling move from selling academic books to selling Mills & Boon romances and we moved to Greece. I have a younger sister and brother, both also adopted. I had I think a happy and active childhood. My mother never worked. She was a strict discipli-narian and could be quite terrifying, but she was well intentioned and highly ambitious for her children. She was also a spender, prone to lavish acts of present-giving, which from a child's point of view was sometimes excellent but also, for me, oddly embarrassing and I was often accused of ingratitude. From the ages of seven to thirteen I went to an enlightened prep school, Downsend, cycling there every day. I was in all the sports teams and near the top of my class academically for most of my years there (they did rankings in those days – a bad idea I think). Much of this was down to my mother's avid coaching.

With other kids I was popular and I had lots of friends. With teachers and other adults I was extremely shy and anxious not to stand out. Accordingly, I performed much better in exams and important matches than in normal school time. The teachers were always perplexed about that. The only serious discord I recall involving myself during these years concerned the adoption issue. I don't think I found out I was adopted until about the age of eight. Certainly both my brother and sister knew when they were much younger, though this was the first time we were all told together. I remember finding some documentation and also being given a booklet by a friend of my mother about children who were adopted. Through these various avenues I deduced that my original name had been Ben Smith and that I'd once had another mother. My adopted status became known at school and certain people exploited it, as boys will do, because they could be sure of a response. At weekends my friends and I used to cycle to reservoirs to go fishing and I remember trashing some poor kid's expensive fishing tackle because he had brought up the subject. I used to see it as a slight on my adopted mother. In honesty I don't think it was really about adoption. I just hated the idea of being seen as different.

Regrettably I did vent this frustration on my brother, Andrew. He's two years younger than me. I don't know if it was part of the adoption agency's strategy but my father's features were passably similar to mine. For years I lied and said he was my real father but had remarried. Andrew, on the other hand, was as different physically to me as it is almost possible to be and also very good at maths and science, at which I was hopeless. People used to ask me why my brother was so different and I used to resent it, and him. He was epileptic from about the age of eight and his fits were something of a school spectacle, which made me ashamed. My mother was fiercely protective of Andrew and I was jealous of that. I was closer to my sister, Kate (four years younger), and used to write and read stories to her. For a couple of years I was quite nasty to Andrew and of no support to him, about which I am now very sad.

For about a year before we moved to Greece there was a panic about money. My mother and father came from different backgrounds. She was privileged and he was a grammar-school boy. Unlike her, he was by instinct frugal, though certainly not miserly. His income was relatively modest and our lifestyle was chiefly funded by her inheritance. Then it ran out and suddenly one year we were holidaying in a guesthouse in Wales rather than Corsica. It didn't matter much to us kids, but for my mother it was mortifying. Worse, my father was thinking of sending us to state schools. For my mother, this would have been the ultimate stigma. She regarded comprehensive kids as barbarians and unfortunately this attitude rubbed off on us at the time. My brother and I had to wear these ridiculous Downsend caps to school and they were routinely knocked off by the state-school kids as we cycled past them, so it was easy to take on board. To avoid what she saw as the unthinkable, my mother urgently escorted me on a round of assisted-places exams for schools like St Paul's and Westminster. I failed them all. They weren't like normal exams but were logic-driven IQ-style tests, at which I had never had any aptitude. My mother was extremely disappointed and frantically dismissive of my excuses. I felt bad but she was only pursuing what she saw as being best for me.

She decided the only thing was to emigrate to Australia. We were booked on the Canberra, *and within three weeks of leaving, when my father landed the Mills & Boon job and we ended up in Athens. I think the money/schools issue may have been just a blind for my mother and that other things were really troubling her. As well as my brother's epilepsy, my sister had been expelled from school for taking drugs, at an unusually young age, particularly for then. I was regarded as the one in the family who was OK – which I was – but then I failed all the exams. I think my mother just wanted us all to start again.*

Up till this point our main concern as children was in trying to predict and respond to our mother's moods. She tended to blame my father for perceived troubles and was the dominant figure in their relationship. He worked long hours, went on frequent business trips abroad and we chiefly saw him at weekends. He was an even-tempered man with a silly streak, which we liked. There was a corridor in the house along which he invariably broke into a limp. He had few, if any, close friends but didn't seem to need any – a self-contained man and one for whom routine was important. We knew when he would be mowing the lawn, pruning the trees, making the bonfire etc and where we stood with him, which was good. He was uncomfortable with intimacy. I don't know if this was just with me or is also true of Andrew and Kate. He was, however, a very dutiful father, always sending us postcards from wherever he was, always bringing back the miniature bottles that I collected, and careful to spend an equal amount of time with each of us. In my case this involved him lobbing down countless cricket balls at my request and trudging innumerable touchlines, where he always stood on the opposite side to where the spectators were.

The original idea in Greece was for us all to go to school there. We started at school in Athens, but there were logistical problems, not least the fact that the school was in severe financial crisis, and we were returned to different boarding schools in England. I went to a terrible place in Leatherhead. It wasn't my parents' fault I went there. I wanted to, because friends from Downsend were enrolled. It was a hateful, delapidated place with an oppressive regime against which I quickly rebelled. My work went downhill, I stopped playing sport and took to underage drinking and bunking off instead. I begged my parents to take me away and, rather hurtfully for them, signed my letters home merely by my school number. They said I had chosen the place so I had to stick with it, which was fair enough. I got in increasingly serious trouble with the school authorities and eventually, when I was fifteen, my housemaster summoned my father from Greece and told him I had no future at the school. This was done in such a way that my father still got stung for the term's fees, and understandably he was absolutely enraged with me.

Back in Athens, the school was under new management and I went back there. My parents decided to forgive me and were hopeful I would change. However, I continued my old ways. I lost so much weight I became skeletal and I also got involved in truanting and fights. Although we continued to live in the same house, Mum effectively disowned me, I felt. My father kept to this line publicly but tacitly I knew he wanted to be supportive. I assumed I would leave school that June, on my sixteenth birthday, and indeed soon after that my father, after considerable effort and expense, arranged a clerical job for me at Mills & Boon's Paris offices. He paid rent upfront on a Paris bedsit and gave me spending money to last me until I settled in. I went there, walked out of the job after two days and went to England to stay with my friends. That was the final straw as far as my father was concerned, too, and now I can't believe I acted like that.

* * *

In England I rapidly ran out of money and was basically in a mess, and I ended up going back to Greece. My brother had already returned there after his health had deteriorated at boarding school. My sister was also back there. Her drug problems were escalating and she was progressing to heroin. They both left school early with no qualifications and I think I would have emulated them had it not been for a couple of teachers who took an interest in me over the summer holidays. At their suggestion I spent the summer writing a thesis on Jonathan Swift. I had developed a wilful blindspot for learning but this time I devoured everything and discovered a whole new world. My parents were highly suspicious of my alleged academic conversion but allowed me to live back at home and go to school.

These teachers were only in their mid- to late-twenties and had both been to Oxford or Cambridge. They made it their mission to get me there too. At the time Brideshead Revisited *was showing on Greek television. I became intoxicated by the idea of it and began sharing the teachers' obsession, though for different reasons. They thought* Brideshead *was faux-camp rubbish. Their support of me really went beyond normal teacher–pupil relationships. They embraced me as a close friend. It was the happiest time of my life. Even before I started studying seriously I loved Greece – the landscape, the day-to-day attitude of the people, as far as it's possible to generalise about that. I worked feverishly towards the Oxbridge exams. I also did things I'd never countenanced before, acting in school plays, running a marathon – the original course from Marathon to Athens: decidedly painful. I came third. My father was more pleased about that than anything. He said it convinced him I had changed. My mother remained icy. She found the idea of me getting into Oxford or Cambridge laughable. In a way I was relieved that the distance between us had been set.*

* * *

I got into Magdalen, Oxford. There I quickly saw that, in real life, foppish Brideshead impersonators were not desirable but insufferable. There was a form of social elitism in operation there – dominated by groups of people who had come from the same major public schools – that, I am not proud to say, I found intimidating. For some reason I had chosen to study history rather than English. I was uninterested and didn't work at all once I went there. I got a Third and was lucky to get that. Still, I had friends and didn't revert to the previous mess. I continued acting and read a lot. I was involved in CND, then at its height, and also in promoting the Oxbridge exam to state schools. I represented the university at boxing and eventually got knocked out. I loved the rituals of boxing training, though I balanced these with long sessions playing pool in pubs and frequenting nightclubs.

It was in an Oxford nightclub that I met my future wife, Susie (who was also adopted). She was quite a prominent student actress. We got married relatively young. I was twenty-four, she a year younger. You have three grandchildren: George, nine, Sofia, six and Xanthe, four. The girls' names are both Greek. I am, obviously, very close to them. George is a wonderful, well-rounded boy, very good at sport if a bit shy. Sofia is the one who I think has inherited the artistic gene. She can both draw and write precociously. Xanthe will be a beauty, I predict. She also seems extremely silly at present, but perhaps it is too early to tell! I wish I could say things are good between Susie and me, but the truth is they aren't, and haven't been for some years, though I wish they were. Quite honestly I don't know how much longer we can keep the marriage together. Anyway . . .

Most of my twenties I spent being a journalist, first a sportswriter and then an investigative reporter. I worked for a succession of national broadsheets and also made some TV documentaries. I had a strange four-year interlude where I managed a boxer called Colin 'Sweet C' McMillan. He was not a puncher but his moves were balletic. We had known each other from when I was a sportswriter. He was going through a tough time, no one seemed to believe in him apart from me, so we got together. More through his talents than my deal-making he became world champion and for a year or so I was jetting to Las Vegas. He lost his title in his first big-money fight because of a dislocated shoulder. He was never the same afterwards and had to retire. Because of his success I received approaches from many top boxers for me to manage them but I declined. The promotional side of boxing was evil. Colin was special, and I felt if I took any more on I would just become a pimp.

In the event I have written two books – good reviews, one literary prize (the Somerset Maugham Award for writers under thirty-five) and absolutely appalling sales. I have been published in America, with similar results. Privately, you don't do it for the money, but it gets to the stage where you think it is too selfish to continue. Also the isolation gets to you. I am compulsive by nature and sometimes I have crossed the line. The writing of the last book was particularly arduous and I ended up in hospital several times. I started getting these physical jerks that I couldn't control. At first they thought I was epileptic but it turned out to be a minor neurological thing. I am better now, and off medication, though it has taken over a year. The narrative voice was very strong in that book, *it almost possessed me, and I think my brain just tipped over for a bit.*

My adopted parents still live in Greece and we communicate with each other rarely. My father writes to me from time to time, which I welcome. They are effectively bringing up my sister's child. Kate lives in Greece too and is still battling heroin. For years I took it as my mission to try and save her but it was futile. Only she can do it and I know it is going to be hard for her. Andrew and I are now firm friends. In fact, all three of us are close.

Anyway, this letter has ended up far, far longer than I had intended, also unfathomably more introspective than necessary and I hope you weren't bored. The truth is that at the time of writing I don't know your address, or even if I would send this if I did. I suppose it comes down to thinking that, if you decided not to respond, at least you'd know most of what there is to know.

So, there it is.

Yours,

Jonathan Rendall

11
Devon

We exchanged letters. She had pleasing hand-writing. She confirmed that my father was Brian Phillips. He had been an undergraduate at Oxford. She was working as a secretary. He denied paternity. He said he could produce ten witnesses to say it wasn't him. He got a Third but was a good sportsman. Years later they met up and he accepted he was my father. They were sitting in Marianne's car at the time, in London, where he worked. He asked what had happened to the baby. When she told him it'd been adopted he was angry. That's what she said, anyway. 'He was the love of my life,' she told me on the phone. 'But he was a bastard.'

She told me about her mother and father. Mimi was still alive, living nearby in Devon, in her eighties. Aubrey, my grandfather, had died quite recently, in his nineties. When Marianne had me, she had driven down to Devon from Oxford in her Mini with me strapped to the back seat.

Mimi wanted to take us in, but Aubrey said 'no'. He didn't want 'a bastard in the house'. Mimi had felt guilty about this all her life, Marianne said.

Marianne had two sisters, Rosie and Anthea, and a brother, David. Another sister had become ill and died as a child. Marianne and David had been particularly close. But Aubrey preferred the company of girls and drove David away. When he was old enough he emigrated to Canada to become a deep-sea diver. Once when he returned, Aubrey was particularly cruel and Marianne smashed a plate in front of Aubrey in protest.

Aubrey had inherited a lot of money when still a young man. He bred racehorses and whippets, smoked untipped cigarettes and drank whisky. When decimalisation came he refused to accept it and continued paying in pubs in old money. His daughters, from what Marianne told me, still doted on his memory, even though he seemed to have spent his adult life dissipating the entire Smith fortune.

* * *

I went down by train. The next day, most un-usually, I had to go to America for an article. I would spend the day and evening with Marianne and then get the night train to Gatwick. It was a bit ridiculous but somehow it couldn't wait.

At Reading I had to change trains. My head began to swirl. What the hell was I doing? I missed three trains. I went to the wrong plat-form. I couldn't think. Finally I got on the right one.

The hours passed in a flash. I tried not to think. I tried only to examine the landscape shoot-ing past. After the stop before Totnes I was the only one in the carriage. I started to cry, un-controllable weeping. I didn't know why. I wished it would bloody stop. It did, just as the train pulled in.

She was standing at the station gate. I recog-nised her immediately from the photos she'd sent. She wasn't crying either. She looked very attrac-tive. The way she was looking at me – no one had ever looked at me like that. I could have done anything, turned around and got on the next train back, and she would have looked at me in the same way. That's what I thought. That was the difference.

She drove to the intersection in her old Renault. It smelled of dogs. That was good. It was a while since I'd been around dogs. She said: 'I promised Steven I wouldn't, but sod it, do you fancy a drink?' We went to a hotel bar. The Royal Seven Stars. It wasn't difficult talking. It was easy. It was like a first date where the introductions had already been made for you.

At the cottage, Steven was huge. He must have been twenty stone. He was a crab processor, her third husband. He used to be a fisherman. Before that he had been an advertising executive in London. Between the advertising and the crabs he had also run an off-licence in Devon. He implied that this choice of profession had not been a coincidence.

Steven did the crab-processing in a room by the kitchen. He'd given up drink. Now he just drank apple crush. He once bought thirty-eight bottles from Somerfield. He drank them from his old beer tankard. He kept the bottles behind the sofa.

The three of us sat in the kitchen. Steven talked for about twenty minutes, about his struggles, like the rest of us, with booze, and the significance of our reunion. I wished he'd shut up. I didn't need explanations from him. I hated him. I thought, How did you end up with someone like him?

Marianne was standing by the stove making soup. It was delicious. I like to stand like that while other people are sitting, as well. And I can cook. I must have got it from her. Why didn't he just leave us alone.

They took me to a pub in West Alvington. The Ring O' Bells. It was halfway down the hill. At the end I went to hug her, but she pulled away. She said, 'You're not going to make a scene, are you?' No, I'm not in the habit of it.

Steven drove us to the station in the dead of night. The wind got up and we took cover behind a hut on the platform while we waited for the train. Standing shivering behind the hut I felt a strange intimacy with these people, even Steven, yet at the same time could not quite believe that I was there at all. The train came and I was relieved. I sat in the carriage, smelling strongly of dogs. That was not my normal smell.

Garden Hopping

Marianne was waving through the carriage window. The train began its long journey, and sitting there I was no longer even sure that it really was still me in that carriage.

12
Oedipus Descending

The second time I visited Marianne, a couple of months later, I took Susie and the children down. It was New Year. The Millennium. They were holding a party at Mimi's house. Rosie had lent us her holiday cottage in Thurlestone, a picturesque and monied village on a hill by the sea, near where Mimi lived.

Rosie was a real looker. Unlike Marianne, she had lived with money all her adult life. Her two husbands had been wealthy. Her children went to public schools. When we arrived at the cottage there were presents waiting for all of us, watches and expensive toys. It was very kind of Rosie. The children were delighted. I felt touched, but also a bit odd.

Susie was quiet and almost sullen. I had the impression she thought this was a deluded adventure of mine and that she was just about putting up with it. Although she was adopted herself, she showed no interest in finding her mother. Or, if she did, she suppressed it. Her brother was very against any such searches, thinking it a betrayal of one's adopted parents.

I went to meet Mimi on my own in the afternoon. She was stooped but still elegant. She took my hand and said, 'Welcome back to the family.' There were tears in her eyes. She gave me a medal that Aubrey had won as an amateur boxer. She said it must run in the family.

Mimi said she had herself been adopted. She was in the process of finding her original relatives. I had felt an immediate affinity with her even before she said that.

Maybe it is connected. Perhaps we are a separate species who, once we find each other, are destined to swim together in a shoal.

The party was fancy dress, but no one had told me. Steven dressed up as a clown. He looked, frankly, terrifying.

Marianne was Marlene Dietrich, in a silver wig. I just wore my green suit. She said that was fine. She said I looked handsome.

There were people walking in wearing false

breasts and risqué outfits. Steven liked that type of thing. I looked over at George, Sofia and Xanthe and Susie. They were all sitting on the sofa. They looked marooned and bewildered.

I had broken us all out of our world of White House Farm. But they would get used to it. Wouldn't they? Of course they would. This was going to be good . . .

Steven volunteered to take Susie and the children home early. I stayed. Tom, my half-brother, was there. You could tell he was in the army from his posture and his shined shoes. He was a very nice and kind bloke. Both of them were – Tom and Simon. Unusually nice, though their relations with Steven were edgy. I was very lucky.

The people ebbed away. Steven was taking someone else home. We were in the kitchen, just Marianne and me. She asked me to open a bottle of Cava. There was a stock of it there. I don't know how many bottles I opened. Then she went towards the bedroom. I helped her. But we became entangled on the bed. To tell the truth, for a moment I wanted to fuck her. She didn't know what she was doing, and I think in that instant she wanted to fuck me too.

Christ, Oedipus descending. But at least *he* didn't know what the hell he was doing.

I pushed her away and she pushed me back. She was strong.

We went outside and she fell over. She refused to let me help her up. I looked at her in her silver wig. She was holding her glass of Cava up.

She said: 'Now you know where you get it from.'

I ran back to Rosie's flat in Thurlestone, bouncing off the ancient walls, thinking ecstatically, So, this is it, finally. Home.

That was the first and last time Susie met Marianne. We separated about a month later.

13
The Old Stone Wall

It must have been that spring. I was to caddy for
Marianne in a golf tournament. She had taken it
up a few years before, with immediate success.
She'd told me in the first letters. She was a nat-
ural sportswoman. She'd played hockey for
Devon once.

I had a car then – an old Citroën AX hatch-
back. I took it to Le Garagiste. That's what he
called himself, this bloke. His twin obsessions were
France and Citroëns. 'Will it get me to Devon?' I
asked him. 'No problem,' Le Garagiste said. 'Get
you anywhere, the AX.'

I got there late. Marianne had already teed
off. The golf club was upmarket. The tournament
secretary was faintly disapproving. She said if I
waited by the ninth, she'd come round soon
enough.

I walked out across the course. It seemed almost cut from the steep hills. The sun lit the brown leaves. I breathed in the crisp air and remembered that, though I hadn't known it, I was a Devon lad.

I don't know golf-course etiquette, and had to duck a few times. The only golf course I'd frequented in the last twenty years was a pub nine-holer by Sandown racecourse. I'd played a friend there for a fiver a hole. Absolute carnage, that was.

I reached the ninth. There was an old stone wall by the green. I sat on it, but after asking a couple of groups that went by, I realised Marianne would still be a while. I began to feel a bit conspicuous sitting up there: who's he? Women's-golf voyeur?

I jumped down and went behind the wall. From behind, I could still see the fairway, but they couldn't see me. In the tangled foliage, I noticed this patch had once been cultivated – the outer grounds of some big house. I began to feel silly hiding there among the roots, but also proud of her somehow – ridiculous, really. Marianne came into view. She looked very glamorous. She was wearing a blue sun visor and tight blue trousers.

Her skin and hair were so clean. She looked different from the last time. I watched her lob a chip on to the green. Yes, a natural. She was by far the best player to have come past.

I walked out and grabbed her motorised golf bag. I must have flicked the wrong switch because it dragged me off towards a bunker. I just managed to stop it.

In the bag she had packed me a few things: cheese-and-pickle sandwiches and two cans of beer.

We ate and drank them on the way round, laughing and smoking.

14
Catford Dogs

A few months later I was offered a TV job, and I had to go to Catford Dogs. I was the presenter. The director was a pillock. Clever, but still a pillock. Ashley. I would have walked off had the executive producer not been Roy, my protector. You can count on Roy. He even lent me two hundred and fifty quid once.

I had chosen our special guest for the night. Stella. I had met her once, years before. She looked a bit like Nigella Lawson. She had hated me. But I thought it might be hate disguised as love. OK, not love, but something. She was another writer. They had sent me her first book. She had a reputation as a femme fatale. Well I could do with a bit of that after three days with Ashley. That really was death.

We were hovering around the entrance to the

dog track waiting for Stella to arrive in her taxi. I was staying as far away from Ashley as politely possible, about fifty yards, because he was an incessant conversationalist as well. I had given in, in any case. I had so many ideas, but I could tell Roy was siding with Ashley. I was beaten. What are ideas, anyway?

Plus there was the money.

I also thought that by standing fifty yards away I might create an element of mystique about myself for when Stella turned up.

Here she was. She got out of the taxi wearing a long beige coat. Very stylish. Her dark hair cascaded down the back of it. She looked bloody adorable. I ambled over as if not really aware of what was happening. We're presenters, see. Guests come and go, y'know?

'Jon, this is Stella,' Ashley said with a very ill-chosen sort of medieval twirl. Prat.

'Have we met before?' she said quizzically. As if. She knew.

'I don't think so,' I said. 'But it's very, very nice to see you.'

You smarmy git.

I put my hand out for her to shake. Instead she reached forward and gave me a quick kiss.

Not far off the lips either. Christ, I was in already.

With Ashley and the crew in tow in their annoying fashion I walked her down the side of the dog track as if I was already her longstanding boyfriend. Well, I felt like it. She didn't seem to mind.

We paused by the metal runners that carry the mechanical hare. She knew about the dogs. That was why she was the guest.

'Tell me,' I said. 'Do they ever catch it?'

She said, 'Is that a serious question, or are you just being *faux naïf*, Jon?' Blimey. '*Faux naïf*.' She was intelligent as well as a looker.

And she'd already used my name as well. Beautiful.

I spent the next three hours flirting with her in the bar overlooking the track. She had a lovely pair of knockers that were spilling out of a flesh-coloured shirt. The only problem was that out of my peripheral vision I couldn't tell where the shirt ended and the knockers began.

I decided not to look at all. Not once. A risky strategy. Sometimes you're supposed to look. She reminded me of somebody. Don't know who.

She tipped me thirteen consecutive losers. I thought she was supposed to know. Who cares.

I knew she was staying in a hotel in Pimlico that night. Normally she lived in Newmarket. I would have beaten the hotel door down but unfortunately I knew I had to take Ashley back. Also, it might have been a bit forward. Typically, he was saving on the petrol.

I asked him how the filming had gone. I thought it had gone swimmingly. He said, 'It was totally useless because all you did was flirt with each other.' Charming.

True, though. She said my writing was 'moral'.

I dropped her off in Victoria. I knew she was a mile from her hotel but she insisted. She looked so bloody sweet in her coat.

We were living together within a month.

15
Benders

I am getting to know what Marianne is like. Every time I go down there she wants to go on a bender with me on the first night. She says it's a family tradition and that she does it with 'all her sons'. I don't like it. I know I can hardly talk about drink myself. I have a drink every day, which is more than she does. But I think that is only because she poisons herself so much with these benders.

So she will lay out all the liqueur bottles and we sit opposite each other across the kitchen table but first there is the wine. Bottles and bottles of it. White. And Steven will keep filling up her glass while he sits there amused with his tankard of apple crush. Then he will excuse himself saying, 'Well, I think I'll leave you two to it.' And then he goes off with an expression of great purity and I take over the job of filling her glass.

At first it's all right sitting there. She has far from reached her capacity and there is still the idea that we are 'rediscovering' each other so there is a justification, so we pretend. She tells me about the circumstances of my adoption and about Brian and taking me to Oxford parties in my cot, albeit often differing versions, and I nod and listen but then the wine is gone apart from one or two bottles for later so we start on the liqueurs. Then it changes. She starts to slur and her face changes, it is almost like a mask. I am reminded of what Hemingway said about Fitzgerald when he was drunk. His death mask. And she won't bother to go upstairs to the bathroom any more and will go out of the back door to the field instead, and fall over, and I will inadvertently catch glimspes through the window of her half-naked body wrestling with her clothes, and look away.

Then she will come back in and start the drinking again – it is well into the early hours by now – and just as I am collapsing, something extraordinary will happen. She gets a second or perhaps third wind and her persona changes into that of a wild sixteen-year-old girl. She whoops and giggles and puts music on and urges me to join in the new mood. At first I found it endearing but now I sit there watching her with a strange fascination as she opens the extra wine and says: 'I saw you left some of your dinner tonight. You would never have done that if I'd brought you up. You wouldn't have had the luxury.'

Once she said that in front of Simon, my half-brother. We were all down on the same night and on a bender together. And he said: 'Oh, Mum. Stop talking nonsense.'

Or she says: 'You see you were much better off with the Rendalls. I could never have given you those advantages. You wouldn't have achieved what you've achieved. I was a terrible mother anyway.'

And I ignore her or politely protest, and wish she would be finished, as the dark liquids in the liqueur bottles have become like bubbling vats threatening to engulf us both. Finally she is finished and is preparing a jug of the hot purple hangover cure that doesn't work. I go up first and lie there in the dark, listening to her stumbling up the stairs and mumbling, 'Good night, Jon.'

Sometimes she comes in and hovers by the bed, looking at me, and I feign sleep. Christ, what is happening? Thirty-five years I was all right on my own and now this? The thing is, despite the benders I like it here. I like knowing that she is behind me. Pathetic, really. And maybe that is delusion. Who knows? I don't.

Then when she has gone I open my eyes and look out of the bedroom window, seeing not that view but the one from the kitchen: the steep hewn road that I run up most mornings with the verges like clashing rocks. Yes, there is something atavistic down here. She is tougher than me, and Steven. I am tougher than Steven, however. She can certainly drink me under the table, and Steven's had to give up.

You've got to be tough to give a child up for no real reason.

And then tomorrow the recriminations and the remorse will start and Steven will get his revenge. He will get her out of bed to pick the crabs with their sweet, sickly smell. Then he will make her cook him breakfast and she will stand there by the stove almost gagging. But I think on balance she knows how to handle him. He still needs her more than she needs him. I don't know whether Marianne and I truly need each other.

After the latest bender I went downstairs and called Marianne out of the crab room for a break. I made her a coffee and we stood there in the kitchen, smoking thoughtfully.

16
Falling

Stella took me to the ballet, at the Royal Opera House. She had been to ballet school. She liked the Kenneth MacMillan ballets best. I had to be dragged there.

Then I opened my eyes and it was there – all of it. The truth. The horror and the beauty and the venality. It was in the shapes: what an invention ballet was. Pure art. Nothing had struck me like that since boxing. It was boxing with meaning. When I was a kid and Kate was doing it, I took it for granted, as if Margot Fonteyn had just popped up knowing how to do it all. This MacMillan took it further. He knew what life was about, MacMillan. He knew.

They didn't, most of the audience. How could they? I followed them out at the end. 'Now, where did we park the car?'

I took Stella down to see Marianne and Steven for a couple of days. They had got us a gratis hotel room on the basis of money owed to Steven for crab meat. The hotelier was not best pleased. We all went out to dinner on the first night and I don't think I have ever been happier. My real mother sitting opposite and my love sitting by my side. Even Steven seemed all right that night. At the end of the meal, probably very rudely, I went to sleep in the restaurant on Stella's left breast, thinking, 'It doesn't get better than this.'

* * *

A couple of years passed. Stella and I moved around different flats in different parts of the country. But my children weren't her children. They were another woman's. I could understand. I tried to be as diplomatic as possible. I kept on seeing them. I didn't have a car any more – long schlepps across the country on buses and trains, all sometimes for forty minutes in some wind-swept park. They always seemed very pleased to see me, however. I was terrified that one day they wouldn't be.

It made me think of Marianne. It wasn't so onerous, was it? Yes I do know it's different for fathers. With her it would have been full time. But still.

My work dried up. My computer was now in storage at Andrew's place in Watford. I couldn't even write.

I kept Stella company at hotels with glasses of champagne that she paid for. But she worked hard as well. I adored her.

I applied for Post Office jobs and worked on a building site. We were building a supermarket. All I did was move bricks around. The site was run by Scouse ruffians. They recognised me from TV. They thought that hilarious. Their only aim was to prolong the job. I watched a bloke putting up a sign for what seemed like a day and a half.

I only did it for a week. Stella said she didn't like me working there. She wrote me a cheque, saying, 'Just have that.'

We still went to the Royal Opera House. I tried to think of the first time we had gone – I was holding Stella's hand. It was almost mythic. My darling's hand. I lay on her breast. But these problems . . .

Another year passed, and then another. I didn't talk to anyone apart from Marek. Otherwise it was just me and Stella.

Kate saw a photo and pointed out how much Stella looked like Jay when she was young. I thought about it.

Well, it was true to an extent. But I wouldn't read too much into it . . .

When we had fought, Stella's footsteps in the corridor did remind me of Jay's outside my room at Ashtead.

On those nights I lay there thinking about what I would do with my kids when all this falling stopped. George, for example. Join a snooker club, maybe? That's what I did in my garden-hopping days with Clive. There would be a few ruffians in there as well, but you need a rounded education.

17
Stray Dog

I made for the small park opposite Horseferry Road Magistrates' Court. I was on foot. I didn't have a car, a home or any money bar a few pound coins. It was a freezing winter's afternoon and I had holes in my shoes. The light was sharp and yellow, and gave the cruel impression of warmth. I put my bag down and sat on a bench. That was it, then: life. All over at thirty-eight. Effectively over, anyway. The rest would just be attrition, survival. At best. There was no one else in the park, just a few blackish birds pecking at the water gushing from an ornamental fountain.

There were only a couple of hours until darkness fell but I didn't feel scared. I felt surprisingly calm. Well, a calm interspersed by sudden twitches that seemed to go off in my head, illuminating the park in whiteness for split seconds, like camera flashes. Yes, if I were directing a film that is how I'd show it: terror submerged. Like Harvey Keitel in *Bad Lieutenant*.

It was a shame that somewhere over the last couple of years, like most of my possessions, I'd lost my *Pocket Book of British Birds*. At least I could have identified a few of the little bastards.

I thought of the people I had loved and who had loved me. That seemed like a different me, someone I could now only grasp at, stretch out to and perhaps, one day, be able to copy. At least I still had the letters from Marianne, somewhere in the bag. So it had been real. That was good.

For perhaps fifteen minutes I sat there, cocooned by the temporary need not to do anything. What would I do? I couldn't think yet. It felt so safe in this void. It was almost womb-like. I clung to it. Each minute in it was a luxury. I knew it wouldn't last, and that the terror would begin. No, I wouldn't let it. Those flashes had stopped, anyway.

I watched the birds. They eyed me warily, and I them.

I had left Stella a note:

I AM A STRAY DOG, BUT YOU
WOULDN'T CHUCK A STRAY DOG
OUT THE WAY YOU DO ME.
SIGNED: STRAY DOG

A bit harsh, thinking back.

Animals and humans are not together in most of England. In Greece the previous year I'd lived in a shack by a chicken run. I'd got to know the characters of all those birds, including the strutting, guilty cockerels.

In-it-together theory.

I picked up my bag. Conceitedly I still thought that with a few more minutes I could have got those birds to like me. I scanned the road, looking for her. Maybe she would come to fetch me in her little blue car. I knew she wouldn't, though. The roads seemed empty apart from yellow and white police cars, cruising in search of real and imagined terrorists.

I went to a phonebox and called Marianne. I left a message asking, could I come down? She'd always said I could, whatever our differences. Mind you, Devon is a hell of a way, and Christ knows how I was going to get there. I stopped at a sign by the park entrance. St John's Gardens. It used to be a cemetery. Then in the nineteenth century they put a foot of soil on top and built the garden. I read this from the sign.

I waited and then went into another phonebox to ring Marianne again. I wanted to talk to her. She must be back by now. She wants me to call her 'Mum', but I won't. It's not fair to my half-brothers, who call her that.

Picking up the receiver I remembered that we had the same hair – with ringlets that spill over our high foreheads: most inappropriate in a man, in my view, but there you go. Once at school Clive called me 'Pineapple Head'.

She answered and said: 'Well, the thing is, you only ring when you're unhappy. When you're happy, you don't bother.'

I listened to her words. Wasn't true. Anyway, *darlin'*, where were you for thirty-five years?

I put the phone down on her. Probably shouldn't have, but I did. Well, that was it as far as a roof was concerned.

You see, I understand everything, everyone's motives – Marianne, Steven, John and Jay. They hate that.

The Paviour's Arms was closed – a shame, but what the hell is a Paviour anyway? I picked up my bag and walked back towards the dirty old Thames.

18
Jay Déjà Vu

When Stella chucked me out and I was walking around London in the dead of night I used to remember things. I always walked east first, sometimes as far as Hackney, then north up to Camden and then down south again, to St John's Gardens, by when daylight would have broken.

Things like:

A few years before I had been writing a book in Greece, in the Peloponnese. Monemvasia. It was the same town as Dad and Mum lived in. Well, it wasn't really still a town. It was now a mass of ancient ruins on a hill by the sea, connected to a modern town by a causeway. Most of the locals had moved down the causeway to the new town. The old one was now populated by rich Athenians and foreigners like Dad and Mum who had renovated the ancient houses. Kate lived nearby. She was still dependent on them. She let out a couple of apartments that were connected to their house and that Dad allowed her manage to give her a living.

I hadn't intended to stay near them. But the place Kate sorted out for me spooked me so I moved to one of the apartments. Dad and Mum were away for another month, and I thought I would have finished by the time they got back. The writing went all right but I got sicker and sicker. I became too weak to walk down the causeway to the shops. My teeth turned black and I was two stone underweight. It was just malnutrition. An old crone saw me and started bringing me food parcels. I was doing two thousand words a day. I was flying. I didn't care about my health. I knew I could recover once I'd finished. Then Dad and Mum came back. They were involved in an animal-welfare organisation. There were always sick dogs around that Mum nursed back to health. In the evenings around thirty cats would come up to the gates of the house and she would chuck them dried feed. It was Mum's compulsion. Dad just went along with it although I think occasionally it gave him pleasure.

They were shocked by my condition. Mum

started cooking me roasts to feed me up. I was touched. We had been apart for so many years. It was kind of her. I told Kate how nice it was. She said, 'Be careful, Johnny. To her at the moment you're just another sick dog.'

I had almost finished and was going back up to Athens. Mum was going there too. She said: 'Here's my number. If you get into trouble just give me a ring.'

Kate was right. Before I left Monemvasia I started getting strong again and the old problems surfaced. The apartment was a mess. I was always going to clean it up. One day I found Mum standing in there, appalled. It wasn't that bad. I said I'd deal with it. She said: 'I bet you don't.'

I finished the next chapter. Now I only had two more to do. I could do them at the Athens hotel. I said goodbye and walked down the causeway to the bus. At the gate Dad said, 'Amazing, you cleaned the whole place up!' But of course I did.

I met Kate at the bus station. I was virtually out of money and she gave me some. She had loads of it around. She was living with a guy called Demitri, a junkie. Kate told me his family were gangsters. He ran a campsite where soldiers and hookers hung out. He seemed OK, if a bit distracted. Shortly afterwards he died from a drug overdose. His mother was the crone who had brought me the food parcels.

In Athens I did one and a half chapters and then realised I hadn't eaten for several days. I was in Glyfada, the district near Piraeus where the American bases used to be. I knew there was a McDonald's down there. It wasn't ideal but I needed some emergency food and I also knew I could get it down. I walked down there and ate it but it gave me no strength. I couldn't walk the four hundred yards back to the hotel. I looked up the dusty dual-carriageway, turned round and hailed a taxi. I rang Mum from the hotel. I said: 'You know what you said about being in trouble . . .'

She picked me up and took me to an expensive fish restaurant. We picked out our fish from the chiller in the kitchen. The staff were real pros and it was charming. Mum seemed to enjoy it.

* * *

Just after I had separated from my wife, and more than a year since I'd last spoken to Mum, I was walking on the platform at Cambridge station when my phone rang and it was her. 'You are disgusting,' she said. In anger I rang her back and told her to fuck off. My God, I had just said that to her.

About two years later I went back to the same town in the Peloponnese. Andrew was out there as well. There was something going on from Dad and Mum that he was now our leader. I could tell it. Sorry, but it doesn't happen by decree. It was affecting Andrew. In a bar he wanted to fight me. I declined. If I hit him properly I might kill him. I found myself crying at what it had come to, for no reason. He said: 'That's the first time I've made you cry.' I was glad for him for his deluded pleasure.

They were going to a taverna with Dad and Mum. I hadn't been invited but Kate said I should come, to bury the hatchet. After five minutes Mum got up and left. I got in the car with Andrew and Kate and drove off. We saw her ahead on the road, marching into the dark. I looked round at them to see if we should stop, but they looked uneasy, so we drove on into the blackness.

I went back to England and back to Stella. I don't know if Dad and Mum had tried to get in touch. Stella didn't like the phone plugged in. I think they were under the impression that I was on the street.

Andrew got me a message. Dad wanted me to sign some papers. Apparently some of his property was in my name. I agreed, of course.

He owned a flat in Kew, near Richmond. I'd lived there for a while earlier that year. They hadn't wanted me to. But they'd forgotten I had a key. I'd thought they'd offer it to me as a bolt-hole for a few months. No one else was living there. But then I realised that they would never offer so I just moved in. I didn't look after it. I spilled wine, ran up a phone bill and wore the suit Dad left there for when he came to London. I wasn't proud of it. I wouldn't have done it had they offered. When I'd had success, they'd basked in it. When I heard they were coming over I picked up my stuff and left.

Now I walked from the tube along the verdant Kew avenues again. I signed the papers. Mum wasn't there. They had brought over another stray dog to find a home for. He was a beautiful grey mongrel with a touch of Alsatian. I got on with him immediately. He recognised that I knew the in-it-together theory.

I talked to Dad for a while, said goodbye to

the dog and walked back out again towards the tube. After about a hundred yards Mum pulled alongside in their Discovery jeep. Dad must've told her I'd just left. She said she'd take me to the station. I said that wasn't necessary but I still got in.

She looked straight ahead and said, 'You're a big boy now.'

I didn't know what to say.

She turned and put her hand on the back of my head. She was stroking my hair. She had never done that, even when I was a kid. I was spooked.

She said, 'We love you really, you know.'

She seemed in a reverie. I wasn't even sure it was me she was stroking. Maybe it was the child she'd never had. The car stalled, and I got out, thanked her for the offer of a lift and walked back out into the leafy green.

19
Jill, the Girl from Barnardo's

Despite my telephone row with Marianne I decided to go down to Devon anyway. Steven had sent me a ridiculous letter. Outraged of Kingsbridge, on her behalf, but I ignored it. Who the hell cared what he thought anyway? They were away. There was a woman called Jill who was at the cottage dog-sitting. Marianne had always said I could go down any time I wanted. It was now my home, wasn't it? Well, I knew that there was an element of fantasy about that, but I decided to ignore it. Also it really did feel like home, that cottage. I couldn't get hold of Marianne so I rang Jill instead at the cottage and she said, 'Of course, darlin'. Come down.' I needed to do some writing. I had never met or even talked to Jill before. Walking into the cottage, I could immediately tell that she was rather extraordinary. I mean that she was an alpha, and not your normal run of person.

Jill was in her late fifties. She was diminutive, about five foot one inch, but athletic, with short hair and a cleansed, youthful face. She wore no make-up, only perfume. We got on immediately. After five minutes she was calling me 'Jon-Jon'. Yes, I thought, a kind person after all those ruthless fuckers that you meet. With Jill you knew you could let your guard down for once.

She was a Barnardo's girl. Her mother had put her in there when she was two. She had had a terrible time. The matrons used to shake her as a little girl. She remembered their faces and was convinced they were getting sexual satisfaction out of it. She'd had some brothers but they'd lost touch. She remembered everything but said she tried to forget. She did not want to be called a 'Barnardo's girl'. She said: 'I want to be called "Jill, the girl from Barnardo's".'

We were standing in the kitchen at the start, me still holding my bag.

'Here we are, Jon-Jon. I made you a meal.'

Jill and I fell into a routine. I would write and she would cook and do her *Telegraph* crosswords. She was good at them. She also had a great command of aphorisms.

After a while she started calling me 'Mister'.

'Here's one for you, Mister. "Fighting for peace is like fucking for virginity."'

She would roar with laughter but sometimes fall silent and sad for no apparent reason. I thought she was one of the most acute and sensitive people I had met.

Once she had run a successful restaurant. Then one day she just collapsed in the kitchen, sobbing uncontrollably. A doctor placed her in a psychiatric hospital for two weeks and this, she said, straightened her out. When she walked the dog, Bess, a large and likeable black Labrador, Jill would often break into a run. In fact she broke into runs even without the dog. You could see she was a natural athlete. She had been a champion schoolgirl sprinter. When her ex-husband tried to attack her, she said she'd knocked him out with a single punch.

She drove her car like a man. More like a rally driver, actually. I knew why she broke into those runs. She was a garden-hopper, like me.

Stella came down to see me, staying at a hotel in Totnes. Jill lent me the car. It only cost her three hundred and fifty pounds but it was a runner. As I left she shouted: 'And make sure you get your leg over!'

When I got back from Totnes I was writing night and day on Strongbow and cigarettes, but I was suddenly weakening. I had one section left to do. I was slumped over the computer. Jill came upstairs with a sandwich, put it on the desk and said, 'You can do it, kid.'

I finished the writing and that night we sat across the kitchen, listening to Janis Joplin and 'Rise' by Gabrielle with our heads bowed. If you are sensitive you can only listen to Janis Joplin rarely. It's the same with Marvin Gaye and Otis Redding with his 'Mr Pitiful'. They are so vulnerable and sincere that it is almost too much to take.

Marianne and Steven came back and it was different. I had rung Marianne from the cottage and she'd seemed delighted I was there. Now Steven said pompously: 'We're very pleased that you felt able to do this.' I could tell Marianne was jealous of Jill and wanted her out. Jill hadn't realised. How the hell could Marianne be jealous? She was my mother.

OK, I know. It was different. No history.

Jill came down with her things to say good-bye. I was sitting with Marianne at the kitchen table. Jill said: 'Oh, look at you two. Beautiful.'

20
Imposter

Stayed down in Devon at Marianne's. Got a bar job at a pub attached to this hotel.

Christ, a bar job. Again. After all these years. Well, sod it, someone's got to do it.

At least while I was serving the drinks I wasn't drinking them.

Felt pretty sharp actually. Running again. The best for a few years.

The management were quite sadistic but sod them, too.

Put the bottles in the main bin. That was one of my jobs. Didn't even think about it. Went into a sort of trance, really.

Got a short haircut. Dressed common. Told them I was thirty-three.

Steven delivered crab meat to the pub. All the people in the kitchen clearly thought he was a complete tosser but I couldn't possibly comment on that.

I brought the children down twice. Steven came into the pub with George once. The second time Marianne and Steven couldn't really be bothered. Evidently all too much for them.

George said, 'Dad, you know when you were standing behind that bar? You didn't really look like you.'

I suppose I didn't. I wouldn't give those bastards one tiny bit of me.

He really is clever, Georgie-boy.

Suddenly got the impression that I might be regarded as an imposter. Particularly from Rosie, my new aunt. She seemed infatuated by the attention of men.

Well, she was a looker. There was no denying it.

Sat on the beach beside her when the summer started and the children were down. That was when I realised. I was trying to monitor George's progress on a distant rock at the time. He didn't seem too clever about it. I was slightly worried I'd have to rescue him.

Glanced round and caught Rosie looking at me. Cold.

You are an imposter, that look seemed to say. Don't think you're really part of this family.

What d'you think I'm going to do, steal the family silver?

It occurred to me that Marianne might think like that sometimes. Jesus shit.

Went and got Georgie from the rock.

Sometimes I went round to see Mimi after my afternoon shift at the pub. I loved Mimi. She had become frail and could hardly see, but was full of life and very straight. Sometimes I brought her audio-books from the library. She didn't think I was an imposter. Once she said: 'Tell me, what do you think about the *Weakest Link* and that woman, what's she called?'

'Anne Robinson,' I said.

'Yes,' Mimi said. 'What do you think?'

'I think it's a total line-crosser,' I said. 'It seems to me a celebration of sado-masochism that is very revealing of the British character.' You could talk to Mimi plainly.

'Oh, good,' she said. 'That's exactly what I think.'

Served Steven's daughter in the pub.

She said, 'I see you're still using Dad's car.' And she'd been rather friendly before.

Imposter, see.

But that's all right. It's just the truth coming out.

Took the bottles out and had a fag by the bins. Some bloke in a hotel uniform told me to put it out. Told him to eff off. He did, thank God, as he was a big bastard.

21
Barman's Cocktail Hour

I had been down in Devon over a month. Marianne had said again that I should stay there as long as I wanted. Being a barman was not exactly the career move I had expected, but these things happen after divorces. I avoided benders and talked to Marianne about the 'war-chest' I would get together – enough money to rent a place and strike out on my own again.

At first it was all right. I knew Steven would resent it but I thought she would keep him in line.

I got the bicycle out from under the tarpaulin. It was drizzling and then holding off. If it really rained I'd be in trouble – sackable offence in that pub, serving drinks in drenched clothes. It may have been a pub but it was attached to a four-star hotel. And I needed the job. Didn't they realise that?

I looked at them through the window of the crab room. No, they didn't.

It would only take them five minutes to run me up to the hotel. Literally, five minutes.

They hadn't spoken to me, as usual, and as usual I said 'Good morning!' and they said it back, waiting for me to say it first. I had stopped making Steven his cooked breakfast, however.

Self-sufficiency, man. It's the only way. A few more weeks and I would be out of there. That's what I thought, putting my foot on the bicycle pedal and starting up the hill.

It was four miles. I loved that ride – sorry to say, Marianne. But you don't understand. To you it's all about who uses the bloody car. I couldn't care less. I'd have ridden in every day. I just didn't want to get the sack.

The previous night I'd known. It came like a stone dropping on my stomach. My own mother not wanting me there. OK, she wasn't really my mother in that way. And it wasn't exactly the first time, was it? How stupid I'd been. Well, if I'm not welcome I won't effing stay.

The hedgerows closed in. This bloke called Ken understood about hedgerows. He'd told me about them. He was a regular down the pub. He was on a bike, too. He was about sixty-five. He specialised in getting drinks off the rich-oes. That's what he called them. Rich-oes. He wore a kerchief round his neck like a right yokel. He had it down pat.

Once Ken stored four cans of Strongbow in a hedge outside Salcombe. He was going to pick them up when he cycled back up the hill. But then someone cut the hedge. All that was left of his cans was little metal ringlets. Nevertheless, a very intelligent man, Ken.

Cycling up the hill outside Thurlestone, I had a terrible thought: sleepwalking. Had I done it last night? And where had I gone? A very ominous feeling. Also, something else. I scarcely dare say. But maybe it was a dream. The bin. Yes, a dream, surely.

I used to know a photographer called Norman. I shared rooms with him on assignments. He went sleepwalking, and with him it was sleep-pissing as well. Once in Bordeaux we sleepwalked at the same time, down to the same spot in the hotel lobby, but I woke up first, and just managed to stop him anointing a Louis XV chaise longue.

Generally I sleepwalk when something spooks

me. I've woken up starkers in the oddest places: a bus stop in South Kensington; a hotel corridor in Las Vegas. The security guy was holding a gun. He said: 'Don't worry, sir. It happens all the time.'

I put the bike in the guests' car park, by Mr Derby's Bentley and Mr Grose's Morgan. Some staff resent them having flash cars, but I don't. It's just an acting job, bar work. They know that. And if you've got money, you might as well have a stylish motor.

I'd just put out the ice and was going round the counter for a last smoke before opening when the phone rang. It was Steven. He was furious: he couldn't contain it. Something I'd done . . .

Shit, the sleepwalking must have been true. But surely not the . . .

Yes.

I spluttered an apology, but Steven wasn't having it. This was what he'd been waiting for.

'It's DISGUSTING, the bin in your room was half full of . . .'

Ah, so it was the bin. Well, sir, may I say that is a remarkable feat of aiming. Furthermore, I had considerably lined that bin with a Somerfield bag earlier that day – not knowing, of course, what might ensue.

Anyway, it's a line-crosser, ringing a barman when he's on duty. Any barman will tell you that. I had Mike, the bar manager, getting his last fag in at three feet's distance and Ray, the other barman, still within listening distance before he went off to hide his hair gel in the Gents, in case the Spanish bird came in. Ray thought nobody noticed, but everyone knew it was there. One of the regulars said he was going to put Immac in the jar.

I heard Steven ranting, but didn't really hear him. Yes, Ray. He was a nice kid, only about nineteen. Well, nineteen going on something much older. He actually looked younger. He had a Roadrunner tattoo on his right biceps. He'd worked on the fairgrounds. I suspected 'Ray' was one of several aliases.

And I'd known about Ray straight away: not adoption, maybe, but something. It turned out he'd been homeless for two years.

Steven said: 'And if you don't stop this anti-social behaviour then you must GET OUT RIGHT NOW!'

Listen, mate, if you're talking antisocial, what

about eating four tins of corned beef at one go, plus seven bananas, plus slurping four pints of apple crush and a bag of doughnuts. I'd rather you didn't do that by my elegant drinking elbow. Nor, if you're talking about it, walking around half-naked, burping and farting and dragging your twenty-one stones around.

I told him something along those lines and put the phone down. That had torn it. 'Who was that?' Ray said. I told him briefly and he said: 'Most of my mum's men were wankers. I had to threaten to clatter most of them.'

I cycled back after the shift, through the tunnels of the hedgerows, with their spiders and flash-flies and flowers. They were so innocent. I didn't want to leave their sanctuary.

I reached the crest of the hill. Eighty revolutions of the pedals until the road sign. I counted them out with my head down. Usually it was accurate but the wind could alter things. I looked up and the sign was there this time. It was downhill from here. I stopped past the sign and lit a cigarette, looking down at the sea below. A Devon lad, eh. Who'd have thought it? Oh, bollocks to that. I'm coming up to thirty-nine. I don't need a mum at my age, except to look after.

I wheeled the bike up the path to the cottage, over the stones from the beach. Bess didn't like those stones. They hurt her feet. I thought, I've never started a fight in my life, but if Steven wants it . . . The problem was he'd probably have a heart attack, and I'd get banged up for murder. No, stop being childish. It's not the playground.

There was no one there, just my bags put outside. My bags outside . . .

And a note from Marianne: 'You're so arrogant' etc and 'YOU MUST CONFORM' in capitals and then 'I don't really want you to go' etc. They'd taken the spare front-door keys from under the stone as well.

I sat down on the bags. I couldn't go yet anyway. My wages were in the bookcase. And I had another hundred coming that I wouldn't get till Friday.

Soon she arrived. Steven wasn't with her. I went up to her and kissed her, but it didn't work. She just looked angry. She said the way I left crumbs out by the cheese, it wasn't surprising that I'd once had rats at a place I'd lived at. (Actually it was nothing to do with that. That place had had rats for decades.) And the way I left the lights on at night was intolerable, and the doors unlocked, and the car . . .

Well, that wasn't me, Marianne. It was Steven. At first I thought I was going mad. So I started treble-checking everything. Even Ray noticed it. He said: 'All these checks, Jon. Are you going paranoid or what?' And I said: 'I bloody hope so. I don't want it to be true.'

But it was. It was Steven. Sabotage. Jesus.

We were standing across the kitchen table. I told her. Not about Steven, but about the whole thing. I said: 'Marianne, I don't think you understand at all. Anyway, you chucked me out once, so I don't suppose I should be surprised you've chucked me out again.'

'That's blackmail,' she said.

'No it's not,' I said. 'It's the truth.'

I said: 'Well, if you're really going to, you and Steven will have to pay me up. I've only got the money for the train. You can keep my wages from the pub.'

'Fuck that,' Marianne said. 'We don't keep money in the house.'

'Fuck that', eh. For the record, you do. There's bundles of it stashed. Steven told me. And he's only giving you forty quid for the whole week.

I walked outside to my bags. She ran upstairs. At that moment Steven came back down the path. He walked around me with his head down.

He shut and locked the front door with an expression of sanctimonious regret.

I sat down on my bags and lit a fag. I decided I'd smoke it till the end and see what happened. That was the problem, really – not being bothered. That's bad, isn't it?

You see, all this talk of mothers and sons . . .

Then Marianne came out again. She took hold of me and said, 'I'm not going to let you go that easily.' I didn't believe her. It was just a stay of execution. She didn't want me there. I'd thought it was Steven, but it was her too. She grabbed me again and said, 'I should have held you like this when you were a little boy.'

I looked at her eyes. They were dry. I started crying, but not for the reasons she thought. We were both fakes, over all of this. I was ashamed. I wanted her to admit it too. She had no maternal instinct. It wasn't her fault. Some people are like that. That was why she'd given me away. That's why Simon and Tom didn't bother with her much; and why she didn't bother too much with them. Her body had given me the gift of life. I was grateful for that, and so were a few other people. And that was it. End of story.

I looked over her shoulder and through the bitter tears saw their cat creeping up on a pheasant in the field. You've got to give it to cats. They're selfish creatures, but they don't pretend otherwise.

That night, on the late shift, the pub was crammed. Ray and I must have taken almost two grand. The regulars bought me drinks. I chalked them up on the board, but I knew I'd never use them. Afterwards we went to a pub in town – a right dive. It was the only place open: old drunk geezers doing karaoke to Frank Sinatra, and coming out with fighting talk just to prove they were alive.

We ended up in the cellar, 1 a.m., drinking shorts, and trying to lift two beer barrels for a bet. Of course we couldn't. I didn't mind. I preferred the dank cellar to the cottage. Apart from the animals, the cottage was dead. I was just marking time, until the early morning bus.

I left Ray there drinking, and walked up West Alvington hill: a lovely walk, even at that time of night. Once I'd run into Ken from the pub there, wheeling his bike, and we'd admired the view of Kingsbridge spire.

I let myself into the cottage, and sat at the kitchen table with a bottle of wine. Steven and Marianne were upstairs asleep. I'd been happy at this table, when I'd first come down, with the animals lying by the Raeburn, and a first drink on the go. The chef at the pub, Gareth, a right hard nut like Clive, had said he did the same; everyone did in catering. 'You've got to wind down after a late shift, even though you're on your own.' And I'd said you should call it the 'barman's cocktail hour', and he'd said: 'Yeah, that's good. That's what it is.'

I finished the wine and went a few steps to the Raeburn to lie down between Bess and the cat. They were very particular about saying hello, and hellishly jealous. I don't care if that sounds twee. In fact I think that's what's wrong with Blair and Bush: this religious idea of us humans as a superior race.

They each put their paws on me. Goodbye my darlings.

I was terrified of sleepwalking again, and woke up almost before I'd gone to sleep. There was a new note on the kitchen table saying: 'You left eight lights on last night.'

The next morning I walked out before I could think about it all and caught the bus to Totnes. By pure chance a friend was on holiday down there and I got him to pick my bag up and take my wages back to London.

I don't think I'll see Marianne again. At the moment I just can't. Anyway, I'm in the barman's cocktail hour, when you tend to pull out your memories, like songs and letters. I keep playing that Phil Lynott song, imagining myself at that kitchen table. *Whack for my daddy o', there's whisky in the jar o'*.

22
Sebastian

I know what Marianne was thinking. She told me. This is what she was saying to herself:

Jon he now calls himself but he is not Jon, or Jonathan either. Sebastian I was going to call him. Then I changed my mind and called him Ben. But really he is still Sebastian. Brian was a shit. Father was mean, too.

I did love Brian. Steven I don't love in the same way. But Steven has been kind. He has looked after me. If it hadn't been for Steven I don't know what would have happened to me.

And I was Father's favourite. Rosie was second and Anthea third. Father was meanest to David. He really was terrible to him. No wonder he moved to Canada. I smashed that plate because Father was being so mean to him.

And Mother has never got over Father being

so mean about Sebastian. But she was so young when she married him. She could never entirely handle Father.

All the things I had to go through because of Father and Sebastian and Brian. I had to live in a commune in north London for God's sake. I thought Brian would rally round. I thought he would ask me to marry him.

I was as pretty as Rosie then. As a little girl I was prettier. Father trusted me. At the end I was the only one who let him drink. How he loved whippets and horses. He put me on his steeple-chaser, and took a photograph of me in my riding gear. I know Father could be difficult, but I loved him.

I should never have married Mark but he was kind to me for a time. That don at Oxford was, too, but frankly he was too old. Mark was prepared to take on Sebastian but things became difficult for him. We lived at that place in Burton-on-Trent. And then he got nasty. He pulled me down the stairs. He was insanely jealous. But I can't regret it, because of the boys.

When Sebastian found me I didn't tell him about my second husband, Derek, at first because it seemed so ridiculous. He is still around here with his long hair and straggly beard. I felt sorry for him. He used to work in Saudi. He made good money. He'd buy drinks for the whole pub and then no one would take him home. So I did. Then he lost his job and went straggly.

And the jobs I had to do because of what happened with Sebastian. All that catering and bar work. That was how I met Derek. Poor Derek. He used to step over the garden fence at night and know that he was home. Often he never made it to the door. He'd just lie down on the grass. I used to find him in the garden in the morning. I told him to go in the end, and he did without complaint.

And then quite recently Mark turned up unannounced. He parked his car on the shingle and waited. It had been twenty years. Sebastian had found me by then. He was down here at the time. He alerted me about the car. I invited Mark in for tea. I thought Steven was quite good about it, really.

Oh daddy, oh daddy, I'm still your queen
I know I'm a mummy at just nineteen
Oh daddy, oh daddy, but I'm still a catch
Don't chase me through the rhubarb patch

And now Sebastian is here again, staying in the cottage. I can scarcely believe it. But I want him gone now. I am a terrible mother, you see? Even with the boys. I know I always say that but it's true, it's true . . . Sometimes they all hate me. They think I'm just a party girl.

I went to his room at night. We'd had a row. It's so difficult between him and Steven sometimes. He was asleep. I touched his head and he stirred slightly. He said he would stay another two weeks. He said: 'Until then, let's have a ball.' But I know he's planning to go tomorrow. I know he's going to be mean.

I took my hand off his head. Goodbye, Sebastian.

23
When Are You Going to Land?

All the years I'd been thinking about it, this one song had been going through my head: 'Goodbye Yellow Brick Road'. I know Elton is supposed to be naff, but that's not true. That's just because he tarts about a bit. He's a genius. And Bernie Taupin, his writer, too. Tangled childhoods, see. Tangled flowers. They knew.

There was no time left for regrets. Like Bernie wrote, *I should have listened to my old man*.

I did find him. I had his address and everything. I sent him a letter via his college before I got the address. Brian. He named his next child after Natalie Wood. Marianne told me. But he didn't want to know. Or maybe he never got the letter. He probably thinks I'm after money. Or maybe he's never told his wife. I thought of haunting him for a while, but what's the point?

I'm going to write him another letter, though. To his address. Fuck it.

* * *

I was living back in Suffolk, in Ipswich. I was renting my own flat finally and even had an old banger. Totally legal. A Proton. Two hundred and fifty pounds. Apparently it's the national car of Malaysia.

Elton was playing Ipswich Town's ground that night, Portman Road. I only had fifteen pounds. Tickets would be seventy-five pounds minimum. I'd have to parlay it. I went down to the Great White Horse Hotel. I've taken to going there. It's not a Paris salon but it's better than watching TV. There's a Corals opposite. Carl the boozer was in the hotel bar. He goes out with my next-door neighbour, Caitlin. She had been an artist but now she said she couldn't work. She believed evil forces had taken her over. For a while she thought I could exorcise her. She collared me outside my flat and told me what to say. Sod it, I just said it. I said out loud: 'Let these evil forces leave Caitlin's body.' Unbelievable, but you've got to show willing.

I didn't believe her. She'd given up two children and that's what was haunting her. She'd hit fifty and had given up. Now what she liked doing was sitting in pubs with her shocking-pink lipstick, being bought cigarettes and drinks by desperate men. She was like an extreme version of Marianne without the family back-up. Having said that, one day Caitlin showed me some paintings she'd done of flowers years before, and they were beautiful.

I nipped over to the Corals and put a greyhound bet on but I couldn't face watching it so went back to the bar. I had two minutes to wait until the result of the race.

Carl said: 'It's like I told Caitlin. I've got to stop drinking so much.'

'Yes, you have,' I said.

'How?'

'Valiums and cold turkey,' I said. 'It's the only way.' That's true.

I went back over to Corals and realised I had won. Fifty-one pounds. I legged it down to the stadium and bought a ticket for thirty-seven pounds by asserting I was an Ipswich Town season-ticket holder. Elton was playing 'Bennie and the Jets' when I got in. It got even better. It was one of those nights.

I was going to land. I would clean up. The next day I happened to be walking down Portman Road again. Elton was gone, I still hadn't been paid and I had three pounds in my pocket. I felt black for a second but it was then that I saw it: not just Andrew and Kate, or my first girlfriend, Nikki, or Jill, the girl from Barnardo's, but other people, like Scrap-Iron Ryan the boxer and Norman the fraudster and Bunny who loved me and Nicola, Jeremy's sister, who hanged herself with the drawstring of her pyjamas. If only she'd known. We didn't need to go garden-hopping any more. We'd got each other.

24
Letter to Brian Phillips

Dear Mr Phillips,

I was adopted forty years ago and am trying to trace my parents. My mother was Marianne Smith. My putative father was named Brian Phillips. I wondered if it was you. He was at Oxford, at the time. I have written via your college but am not sure it reached the right person so I hope you will forgive this direct approach. If it is you, you might be interested to know I went to Oxford too and am a published novelist. In that case it might be good to meet up or perhaps just correspond, once only if you want, just to know. I don't want anything from you – certainly not to intrude on your life, as I know these things happen. If it is not you, I apologise greatly for this intrusion. I enclose a stamped addressed envelope and would be extremely grateful if you could let me know one way or the other.

Yours sincerely,
Jonathan Rendall

[SENT]

25
Another Letter to Marianne

Dear Marianne,

Thanks for the cookbook for my birthday and for the trouble you spent finding a copy. I know it's a good one and I will use it a lot. I also hope you're well and knocking them in at golf. I'm sure you are. So it's forty years since you had me. As for all the other stuff, I don't know if you want the truth as I see it. If you don't you'd better not read on. I think we are equally culpable in a way. Me for diving in and pretending that you'd been my family all along and you for doing the same. However, I really don't understand why you turned against me so strongly down there. The fact is it started off with the euphoria of an affair and then when we tried to transmute it into something else it was all skewed. I don't think it had to be actually. I had no idea you were canvassing people about where else I could go. I had no idea that my use of the car was such a bone of contention until Steven's daughter accosted me about it in the pub. You said I could stay there for as long as I wanted. That meant a lot to me, having you and the cottage there, but it turned out to be an illusion. You said I could use the car. You refused my offers of rent money and then resented me. It dawned on me that I was semi-regarded as an imposter. The only one who didn't was Mimi and maybe Anthea, both of whom I liked a lot. However, they didn't have to live with me.

Also, and you won't like me saying it, I don't think Steven has helped. And no, I'm not jealous of him as you said. As if, Marianne. On the contrary he strikes me as a particularly jealous and almost maniacal man, a control freak with vulnerable people while being obviously vulnerable himself. I admit it might have been difficult for him the way we were carrying on at the start but I am your son for Christ's sake and I can't escape the feeling that he thinks he has seen me off the same way he did Simon – a quite inappropriate thing to want to do but that's human nature and insecurity generally for you. The difference is

Simon has to deal with it because you brought him up and there is all that history, so he has to. That isn't there with me.

By the way, when I went sleepwalking and I said I had done the other thing before, that wasn't true. I said it to try and make you feel better. The fact is although I have sleepwalked I have never done the other thing either before or since. The realisation that I wasn't wanted at the cottage was shocking and stirred something elemental in me, and that was the result. The worst thing is that until shortly before then I had rarely been happier. I liked standing in that kitchen thinking it was my home. I had got my career back on track and was getting the war-chest together. I knew Steven didn't want me there but I thought you would put him in line, not join him. Now you want everything to be all right again, but have you forgotten that you went on the offensive after I left, accusing me of stealing things from Simon's room, which was preposterous, refusing to give me Mimi's telephone number 'because I was just using you all' and letting it be known that your friend Ellen thought I was a 'devil'? Well I imagine Ellen began thinking I was a devil a) after

I didn't jump on her as she appeared to want when I made those trips to pick up fags and b) I disapproved of her nicking stuff for me all over Kingsbridge. So, yes, I must be pious as well as arrogant. You don't seem to realise how much hearing these things hurts. The truth is some people are hard as nails about their emotions, frankly because they don't seem to have any beyond puddle-depth, but I am not like that and I have to protect myself.

The night before I left I stayed up almost the whole night out of worry that I would go sleep-walking again, so I knew I had to go. I felt you and Steven had declared war on me despite the uneasy truce, and whatever your regrets now I think if you are honest that was true at the time. I thought Steven's call to me at the pub that morning was outrageous. I didn't know I'd done it, and as if I'd have wanted to! He was out of control. Anyway, you've got to say my aim was impressive as regards that bin, given that I was unconscious, but perhaps this isn't the time to joke. I tried to show willing about the crab business, even poring over his accounts with him if you remember, but I can't say it was reciprocated. I don't think either of you understand the business of being a writer.

Soon after you met me I was on TV and had all sorts of fickle friends appearing, but I was never under any illusions. I didn't want to meet your friends who wanted to see me just because I'd been on the telly, for example. It was just luck and I was never going to take their shilling except for something I believed in. I knew poverty would return, and perhaps sporadic future success, or maybe another lucky one. It's the artistic path, if you like. Do you know how many jobs and easy careers I have walked out on to pursue it? It is undoubtedly lunatic from a certain perspective but I know what I am doing, for better or worse, and while I don't expect applause I don't want boos when times are thin. I don't want to stick around anywhere that I'm not wanted. I probably am a nightmare to live with, but amazingly there are still certain people who like having me around through thick and thin, so I'd better stick with them.

Leaving when I did caused me severe problems and I was actually homeless for a short while but thankfully the weather was warm. I now know what a killer the cold can be because recently, without going into it, I was locked out and had to go into hospital with hypothermia.

Otherwise I'm in good nick, still running and in work enough. I'm writing this book, which you will hate, even though I think I will come out of it worse than anyone. I would much rather not be writing it and instead absorbing it into some novel but I couldn't get commissioned for fiction at the time, although that seems to be changing, and I have to write to survive. I am not unkind.

Listen, I am glad and grateful that you had me, I am very, very glad that we met and had good times. Can't we just leave it at that for the moment? I lived the best part of thirty-five years knowing that I didn't have a 'real' family without it destroying me and that's what it's come round to again, if we're both honest. Far worse things happen to people. And no, I am not 'damaged'.

As your eldest son, who has now reached a patrician age, can I say one last thing? Will you please look after yourself? When I finish this book I am going to make swingeing changes to my lifestyle. I mean it. I've had a good innings on the booze and fags and I've never really needed them. Neither do you, although I'm not proposing prohibition. Don't be sad. Please pass

on my love to Mimi, Anthea, Simon, Tom etc
and thanks again for the book.

Your son,
Jonathan

[NOT SENT]

26
Letter from Brian Phillips

Dear Jonathan,

Thank you for your letter which I received a couple of days ago.

I was born in 1926 in the Lake District, and was the only issue of my mother's first marriage to a Bernard Woolley. She was divorced soon after and married a John Phillips – antique dealer of Manchester – who had my name changed to Phillips by deed poll.

Unfortunately, therefore, I am not the person you seek, but would like to wish you every success in your search.

Yours sincerely,
Brian Phillips

27
Identities

The more I think about this adoption business the more I believe – perhaps the obvious conclusion – that it is all about identities. All my life I have had the tendency to take on aspects of other people's identities. I have become them almost, and then slipped into someone else's.

Sometimes it amazes me when people identify me as me. I think they must be mistaken.

Is this down to being adopted? I don't know, but I would say it is a factor. I used to have a cat that I took away from his mother too soon. If I stood a newspaper up on the carpet he would always run under it. Peering at him I knew that momentarily he didn't know who he was. Why should we be different?

But it is only momentary.

I haven't been to a psychiatrist or anything.

Well, I once did go to a psychotherapist for one session out of curiosity, because it was free. He was a six foot six American living on the Suffolk coast, and I came back thinking he was in definite need of psychiatric help himself.

What else?

OK, well as a kid I didn't suck my thumb but was always putting my fingers in my mouth. All the time. The nipple theory, I have since been told. It's true that even when I'm off the booze I tend to have something in my mouth, a cigarette or one of umpteen cups of coffee or a fingernail. I'm sure I don't need to, and I do not regard such traits as life-determinants, but it is interesting.

As a teenager my attitude towards girlfriends was certainly different from my male friends' attitudes. They wanted to 'stay independent'. I wanted to marry every girl. One of my ambitions was to be a father at sixteen. 'A desire to establish the family that you never had', I suppose they would say. Maybe.

I was married at twenty-four. I don't think that would have happened otherwise, actually. Well, I don't. Then divorced. In between, my three lovely children.

Except, that is the thing. That's one thing I

can't really understand about Marianne. Even when I was homeless and skint I schlepped across the country on buses and trains, avoiding ticket inspectors, to snatch an hour with them in some park if that was all that was on offer, to let them know that I was still there and looking out for them.

I am still in favour of adoption, however. It is preferable that there are valid reasons, of course, but I suppose there's nothing you can do about it if there aren't. Adoption is still much better than growing up In Care. In the Catteries.

Andrew found his father. Really he was looking for his mother. His half-brother came over and stayed with him in Watford for months. He was Canadian. I thought he was using Andy. Andy paid for everything. When Andy's money ran out he left.

When you are adopted the decision to search for your parents can, suddenly, seem unquenchable, and the curiosity has to be sated. That's when it becomes dangerous. It is an oddity that many adopted people embark on the search just when they have settled, finally, on an adult identity. I suppose they feel that now they can. Then the findings of the search turn into something far more elemental, or appear to, and throw everything into chaos.

My life became chaotic, to say the least, when I found Marianne. But I am not sure that was down to adoption. That was just a factor. It was as much down to divorce, guilt, love and pursuing the writing life. I had given up so many jobs, and the stability they brought, to pursue a writing career, that I was already used to risk and the ever-present possibility of chaos and penury. I had simply managed somehow to stave them off before. I am aware that attempting life as a writer involves considerable selfishness, and if the breaks don't come you must accept the consequences.

On balance, however, I would have to describe the experience of finding my birth mother as destructive for all concerned. It killed off whatever vestiges of a relationship I had with Mum, though I tried to keep it from her, and put Dad in an invidious position. I'm not entirely sure why that should be, but once you're asked to take sides, that's what happens.

It stirred up deep-seated and troubling emotions in me that I didn't know I had.

I think it hit Marianne worst. She'd made no actual attempt to find me, although she said she did once consider writing to some TV show that reunited lost relatives. I became aware early on that her friends knew about her 'lost son'. She used to talk about him late at night, they said. I think she would have been better off if I'd stayed like that, in the abstract. My actual re-appearance was too much for her to cope with.

Brian Phillips is the one who might be thought to have got away Scot-free, but I'm not sure.

Andrew and Kate can do what they like, of course. But if either of them ask my advice about finding their mothers I think I would say what John from the White Horse said: 'Don't do it.'

28
Letter to Mum and Dad

June, 2004

Dear Mum and Dad,

First of all, Mum, happy birthday, and sorry this greeting is late again. Well, since I don't think we've corresponded at all on this date for a few years, I suppose this performance might just feasibly be counted as an improvement. I hope you had a nice day, anyway. The truth is I have been working night and day on this book and the days flew past before I knew it.

I feel I should discuss this book with you both. It is called 'Garden Hopping' and is a memoir of adoption, nonsensical though that sounds. Do you remember Clive Golding from Downsend? He was a policeman's son and a right hard nut if you remember. You used to get annoyed with me when he rang up and I'd put on an accent. Yes, I agree that was ridiculous and I'm sure it didn't fool Clive for one second. Anyway, he gave me that phrase. Garden-hopping was when you leapt through people's gardens at night. Clive started it and I exported it to the posh kids until people like Adrian Pilkington and Simon Clarke were begging me to take them. We even roamed through the grounds of Parsons Mead girls' school one night. I don't know if you ever suspected any of it. Don't be appalled.

It seemed to me an apt metaphor for the business of finding one's 'real' parents, a process I'm sure you could have done without after all you put in. I didn't intend you to know, actually, as I didn't want to cause any unnecessary hurt, but I think Susie told you. Someone did anyway. What you should understand is that it is curiosity, that then seems to become something else, and then in turn retreats and gets filed under 'curiosity satisfied'. I'm not sure it really is but by then the damage has been done to all and sundry.

I don't quite know how I got involved in this book, but I did and there it is. You would probably disagree with loads of it and be hurt by it. For that reason I don't think you should read it. *It is not, however, born of any malice, merely the need, once started, to tell the truth as I see it, if that isn't too sanctimonious. It was your misfortune to acquire a writer, and I am aware there is intellectual hypocrisy in explaining away any distress this might cause you on the grounds that 'this is what I do'. But at the same time, it* is *what I do. And writing it also causes* me *distress. No one forced me to write about it, and if I weren't I wouldn't be applying my mind to it in this way and the whole thing would have remained submerged.*

I'm not even sure if that's accurate or what I'm trying to say. I suppose I wish you to take the impossibly enlightened view of: 'Listen, he's a writer. Things haven't panned out quite as we'd hoped but let him get on with it and in a way we can regard it as our gift to him.' However, I would quite understand if you thought that indeed impossible.

Yours,

Jonathan

[NOT SENT]

29
Costume Change

Jesus Christ, you're acting as if they give a fuck. Well, maybe they do in a way. Maybe you do in a way. Who fucking knows? But you haven't seen each other for years, and they took your ex-wife's side in your divorce, and the last time you saw Mum it was mad and the time before that she couldn't stand your presence for five minutes. Oh yeah and their friend, Jackie, told you Mum wouldn't have *Twelve Grand*, your novel, in the house. 'That book,' she calls it apparently. Why? It's a novel. It's imagined. It's someone else's life. Bloody proud of creating that life, actually. Almost bloody killed me as well, not that it's relevant. Plus I gave her an acknowledgement for cooking some strength back into me. So what's the effing problem? Jesus H, man.

I walked out of the flat and went to the Great

White Horse Hotel. Carl and Caitlin weren't there and I was relieved. Neither was Cigarette-Holder. I hope she doesn't mind me calling her that, but it's unusual to see someone using one. Her real name is Gracey. She was in Scotland with her sister. Her sister told me all about her when they came round to pick up some cassettes. Homelessness etc. Now she was going to have her own place, for the first time in years. She always dressed elegantly. She was a brave girl. Well, forty-three, admittedly. But to opt in again. Very difficult.

There was only some posh bloke at a table drinking red wine. Mid-fifties. I'd seen him around before. He seemed to know everyone. And then another guy came in wearing a Hawaiian shirt and stood there drinking at the bar, and then after a couple of minutes the posh bloke said to him: 'Oh come on, Gibson. Stop ignoring me and come and sit down. We were at school together for Christ's sake.'

I think he said that for my benefit, to fill me in. He's always seemed to want to speak to me, Posho, or at least to let everyone in the vicinity know what he was up to.

Gibson trotted over meekly and sat down

while Posho spilled a few anecdotes. Finally Gibson said tentatively: 'So, what else have you been up to?'

'Well, I went to the Elton John concert,' Posho said. 'But I'm not a great fan of John to be honest and also I noticed he didn't do any costume changes.'

'Really? Is that right?' Gibson said.

'Mmm,' Posho said. 'None.'

That wasn't true. Elton changed before the encore. He went into a different suit. He'd given his all and had been sweating.

I wondered if a part of me wanted to change back into the old costume. But it was too late. That's life. That really is the test of life, actually. To come back in new conditions.

I put my empty glass back on the bar in a way that barmen appreciate and walked out. I was going to remark to Posho about Elton's costume change but I couldn't be bothered.

30
Instant Family Offer

It was 2003. I was back in London with Stella to give the writing another go and needed a job while I tried to get some journalism and book interest going. I went to the Jobcentre off Horseferry Road and after a few days there was still this one bar job going: a gentlemen's club in Chelsea. Five pounds fifty an hour, no split shifts, weekends free. Contact Mr Kenny Bacon. It had been unfilled for some time. I rang the number from a phonebox. Normally I would have asked for 'Kenny Bacon' but asked for 'Mr Bacon' instead. I could tell that went down well. In a Scottish accent he asked me to come in the following afternoon.

I had no experience of gentlemen's clubs. It mildly surprised me that they still existed. The club stood on a side street, an unprepossessing and faintly austere red-brick building. It was a Scottish club. Well, it was unlikely they would be wanting an Englishman like me. I rang the bell at the tradesman's entrance and tried to dredge up some Scottish ancestry in my mind.

Another Scottish voice instructed me to go round the front to Reception and wait. I sat on a polished wooden bench. Through the doors I could see the inside of the club. It was opulent, if slightly musty. I could see statues, paintings, a wide, winding staircase and, across an expanse of tartan carpet, the high-ceilinged bar where it seemed unlikely that I would be working. No one was in it. No one apart from staff seemed to be in the club at all.

Mr Bacon appeared from a back staircase, telling me to call him 'Kenny'. He was about my age, shorter and stockier. He kept up a for-mal manner belied by a shy face that broke into a squint. He took me down to an office in the bowels of the club. He descended the stairs at what seemed an incredible pace. There is a technique to it, and later I would learn it. The same goes for walking quickly across carpets and corridors while carrying a tray. You spring off your heels. But I would never get as fast as Kenny.

'Do you have any questions, Jon?' he said after a perfunctory interview. He was wearing a black jacket, wing collar, black bow tie and tartan trousers. I had put my name down as 'Jon' on the form. I had also left off almost all educational qualifications, citing only my stint as a barman in Devon. I was fairly sure they would give me a good reference.

'Will the fact that I'm not Scottish count against me?' I asked.

'No bother,' Kenny said. 'The two girls you'll be working with are Vietnamese and Greek. I'm looking for someone to keep an eye on them.'

Kenny said it would be down to what Mr Lane thought of me. I didn't know who Mr Lane was, but he was clearly important. As we ascended to Lane's office in a rickety lift, Kenny told me more about the club. No ladies were allowed in the members' bar. They had to go to the Ladies' lounge. Nor were they allowed in the Smoke Room. It became clear that all 'staff' (with the exception of Mr Lane himself, who it turned out was the club secretary) were to be addressed by Christian names, 'the members' by their titles – Mr, Sir, Lord etc. Kenny spoke of all this as a natural state of affairs. I asked him how long he'd been there. 'Two years,' he said. 'But most staff have been here much longer.'

I saw Lane, and must have passed the test and was measured for my tartan trousers by the club outfitter. He looked up both my original name and my adoptive name and showed me their respective tartans. 'So you see, you're Scottish after all,' he said. The work was easy. There were never more than a few people in the bar. I eschewed the staff canteen in favour of walks to the bookies. Kenny was fine about that.

We worked in tandem with the members' dining room upstairs. On each side of the dining room was a banqueting suite. Sometimes I had to take the cigar humidor up, and offer it round. Edie was in charge of banqueting. She was a thin, elegant Scottish woman in her fifties who could be quite fearsome. Her accent was often impenetrable. She called me 'son'. She had two sisters who also worked at the club, in house-keeping. All three were regulars in the staff smoking room. They wore the same rings. They had been at the club for twenty years.

Upstairs the wine waiter was Tommy, a Glaswegian. He had a little room by the first-floor stairwell where he kept his stock. He called it his 'office'. He was my age and size and had a hyperactive, boyish air. He was a rabid Rangers fan and the club's prize asset. Members competed for his attention and were always asking him to drink with them, or donating him the dregs of their expensive wines. If members insisted, you were obliged to drink.

When there were dregs around, Tommy always shared them out. The code word for it was 'detention'. He called me 'big man' or 'daddy-long-legs'. 'All right, big man!' He had a cat that he took for walks like a dog. He always had scratches up his arm. If you asked him how his cat was, he would say: 'Terrible, big man. Went up another tree.' Then he'd roll up the sleeves of his green sommelier's jacket to show you his new scratches.

I signed my contract. There was only a week's notice, so that was all right. With the contract came a chart showing the command structure of the club. Mr Lane was at the top. I had already been inked in near the bottom, along with Anna (Vietnamese) and Paola (Greek). Tommy and Kenny were somewhere near the centre. I soon realised this was not some bar job. You were, with a few modern adumbrations, in nineteenth-century service.

Service was fine by me. Better, in fact. I wasn't intending to write about it then, but in a wider artistic sense, it was better material. After all, I wasn't really there.

The months passed. Whenever a member of staff left, we all went to the Horse and Groom. When Big Darryl the chef left, there was a girl from the kitchens there. I don't remember her name. Tommy called her 'wee man'. She looked at me and said: 'The club is very clever who they hire. We all end up thinking it's our family.'

What?

There was a Staff House in Hackney, where some of them lived. Fifty quid a week, taken off your wages.

In the next few weeks, something happened. The newspaper column I had been promised was deferred. No publisher interest. And suddenly, in an almost uncontainable glare, it all seemed real: the club, the staff smoking room, being in service. It terrified me. How stupid I had been. The club was my lot, like it was for the others. I was no different. How arrogant to think I was. In a way we were chosen. I should be grateful, as long as I didn't end up in the Staff House. That, I couldn't face.

Now that I knew the job was important, that for the moment it was all, career-wise, I had, my performance went to pieces. I began dreading going in. I dreamt about it: whole literal dreams of the duties I would perform at the club. Then I would wake up, and go and do what I had dreamt. My mind started playing games. Sometimes you could wait hours before serving anyone, and standing there I would think: when the next person comes in, and you go to serve them, your hand will shake uncontrollably. It will shake so badly that the glasses will fall off the tray. I did shake, too. I spoke to Tommy about it. He said: 'Ay, I get the same. Sometimes, when I know I've got to serve Mr Lane, my hands shake so bad he asks me if I'm ill.' You see, I had realised that good service comes down to sure movements of the hands. Yet if they are betraying you, what is there left?

I now knew I would be there for the summer. In August, the club shut down, but the bar stayed open. Before it closed, we all got our sum-mer bonuses. I got the lowest of anyone: about seventy pounds. Tommy got over five hundred.

A members' committee decided the figures. I was hurt. But now I knew which members decided it, I could act. I would get in with them. There were the Christmas bonuses to come, and then next year's summer ones.

Christmas? Next summer? What was I talking about? I must be going mad.

I had thought August would be a breeze, a chance to re-group. But it wasn't.

The weather was incredibly hot. For day after day it was almost a hundred. In the afternoons the sun hit the bar. It seemed like a furnace. To move some furniture, I stripped down to shirt-sleeves. Mr Lane caught me. 'Jon, where is your jacket?' I'd had enough of my shakes, and to take them on, I took to roaming the club with my tray, dispensing cold drinks to the remaining staff, daring the shakes to assail me. It was like being at war with your own mind. Edie and her sisters used to sit in the staff smoking room with the lights off. They felt the darkness made it cooler. Sometimes when you went in there, you didn't see them at first. It was because of their black dresses. Then you'd make out their faces drawing on cigarettes, like ghosts. 'All right, kid?'

By September everyone was back, and I'd had some good news. My newspaper column was starting, and publishers wanted meetings. It was only that they'd been away. Overnight, my shakes vanished. I threw myself into the service game with new relish. Performance-wise, I was still way behind Kenny and Tommy, but I felt I was improving. Then I realised I didn't really have to work there at all any more. Let's face it, the pay was terrible. I put my notice in to Mr Lane, but he cornered me as I was speed-walking with my tray across the tartan carpet.

'Jon, how would you like to continue working here, but part-time?' he said.

'I would love to work here part-time, Mr Lane,' I replied.

So it continued. Mr Lane put a card up on the members' notice-board, about my column. I don't know what it said. I was too embarrassed to look. I became aware that almost all the members now knew my name. It had taken five months, but they did. Paola said she didn't know what I'd ever been worried about: 'It's me who should be worried. You, they like.'

In a way, I felt it was too late. Things seemed to me to be getting a bit out of control. The bar was busier than ever. Banqueting was thriving. Dregs and detentions were everywhere.

I don't drink whisky, but I seemed saturated in it. The smell of it came off the pores of my fingers, from the silver measures that I poured for Mr McSweeney. It came off my clothes and my hair.

One night at the club, Mr McSweeney played Mr Higson at snooker for a million pounds.

I'd had to leave Stella's place. I was living miles away. A sixty-pound cab ride. The club paid unquestioningly. I kept telling Kenny, but he kept talking me round. He got me a room in the Staff House, but I never went there. No.

We all end up thinking it's our family.

It was a Friday night, and I somehow knew it was my last one. I heard a noise upstairs, and realised Tommy was still there in his 'office'. I bounded up, shouting. Why not. One last detention. We had the dregs, and then walked out. He was carrying sixteen empty glasses on his tray. He tripped and dropped them. They shattered down the steps, covering them in a crystal carpet. We watched them go. He said: 'I don't know about you, big man, but after that, I could use a drink.'

That Monday morning I decided I wouldn't go in. I rang Kenny from a payphone. He gave me an earful. I sent him fifteen pounds cash, all I could spare – drinks-money at the Horse and Groom for covering for me. And a note signed 'R/CFC Alliance'. Rangers and Chelsea. That was our toast. Him, me and Tommy.

31
Watford

I needed to go to Watford. Andrew lived there and was storing my computer. He loves Watford. The way he talks about Watford you'd think it was 1920s' New York.

I don't agree with him about that but I don't mind the place. It's just somewhere people live and get on with it. I prefer Watford to Devon. In Devon people are too proud of living where they do. I like Suffolk from an aesthetic point of view, but then I'm privileged, because unlike most people at the Great White Horse I actually work. Too many people come to Suffolk to opt out, and they can. So on balance Watfordians are more admirable than even Suffolkians.

So Watford is just a word for people who don't opt out. I know Kate lives in Athens but really she is striving for Watford. I think she can make it. Andrew has opted out for the time being but I know one morning that will change and anyway there is the mitigation that he is literally a Watfordian. Marianne *has* opted out I think. Mum has never had to choose between opting in or out, and there is a whole class of people like that. Steven purports to opt in but I'm not so sure he's not still opting out. Dad has opted in. I have opted in. Stella has opted in more than anyone I know except Jill, the girl from Barnardo's. Caitlin has opted out while pretending it's illness. Carl believes her and has himself opted out for some time but funnily enough I reckon this whole experience might enable him to opt in again and reach Watford. Likewise Cigarette-Holder. I think she has set her sights on it after years of opting out and just from the way she now carries herself I would bet on her to get there.

So, we'll all meet in Watford, yes?

I was thinking all this along the rushing green of the Watford road. It would be the Proton's last journey, as the tax had run out. I hoped it was enjoying it. When I got there Andrew had set the computer up on the table. He didn't need to do that. He's a lovely bloke, just allergic to work. He's going out with a Czech girl, Denisa. He calls her 'Dennis with an A'.

'What's happening, Andy-boy?' I said, walking in.

'Oh, the usual shit,' he said.

'What's that?'

'Doing absolutely fuck-all.'

We both laughed. I telephoned Kate from his place. She was fine. I was proud of her. To kick heroin – it's a hellish thing to do.

I printed my stuff up and walked out with him. He had to meet Dennis with an A. I clasped his hand in the dark and he clasped mine back. I headed to the Proton.

I called out, 'See you later, bruv.'

32
Hello and Goodbye

Note from Marianne written on half an envelope, September 2005. At my request she was sending me back my childhood memoir, 'The Day Before':

> You were born at the Radcliffe in Oxford –
> not Nuffield Maternity Home. Let me know
> how things go, and keep your promise of
> letting me have this back. Love
> Mxx

33
Brian's Kind of Music

Through a process of elimination I found him. He had qualified as an accountant. I already knew from Marianne that after Oxford he had started work for a large national firm. All the others had ruled themselves out. There were other things. It was him. No doubt. An affluent-sounding address in a village in the southeast.

He had not returned my stamped addressed envelope so I drove out there. I was driving Stella's car. She was with me. I didn't want to fall apart like I did about Marianne at Reading station and I knew that with her there I wouldn't.

Actually I didn't think that would happen anyway. I wasn't worried about Brian, somehow.

I wasn't going to knock on his door or

anything. I wouldn't signal my presence. That would be inappropriate.

No, I would just size the place up and try to get a feel about him from his house and his car and the way things were ordered. If he happened to come out, of course, that might be different. I might say something, yes. But what the hell would I say?

'Hello, Dad.'

I don't think so.

Actually, I think I would just get out of the car and say politely, 'Brian . . .' And then whatever came out would come out. Nothing emotional. How could it? Civilised. Come on, I was used to such conversations with strangers from serving at the club.

Yes, a stranger. And even if he did come out I was sure we would be quite different. Me, an accountant? With my financial history I would qualify as an anti-accountant. Easily.

Coming off the motorway my stomach was in turmoil. My head had gone. We got to the village but couldn't find his address. We went to a pub to take stock. I started to shake. Stella had to get my drink from the bar.

Christ, falling apart again. And I'd thought

this might be a bit of a jape. How mysterious. There really must be something elemental in it . . .

I remembered a photo Marianne had shown me, from the 1960s. Had that been him? Hadn't she said that when she took the photo from under the record player? Couldn't think. It might have been. It was during a bender.

'What did he look like?' Stella said.

'Well, I'm not sure it was him,' I said. 'But I suppose you could say a generic member of the Rolling Stones, without being a midget.'

It was a Sunday. Maybe he was having his Sunday lunch there. She scouted the pub for likely suspects. The only one who fitted the age profile was a ruddy man who looked like Arthur Askey. No. Well, don't think so, anyway.

We left and found his address finally. It was the last house left in the village. I asked Stella to drive. The house was up a private track in woodland. It was beautiful and isolated round there. She stopped the car by the 'Private Road' sign. There was only his house at the end. I said: 'Go on, go on up there.'

She drove up and stopped by the gate to the house. I looked at it. It was a large white-faced house facing a lovely garden. But there was nothing poncey about it. If I had a house like that, that's exactly how I'd have it. There didn't seem to be anyone there. I sat in the stillness for a few seconds and then a noise intruded.

It was music. Music coming from the house. At first I thought it was an old Blues record but then I realised it was ragtime jazz. Someone like Louis Armstrong. An early recording.

Christ, he was in there, listening to music, probably with a glass of wine. I do that. Not many people do actually. They can't amuse themselves.

Of course, it might not have been him. It could have been his wife, or one of his daughters, or someone else entirely. But no. Instinctively I felt it was. It was the music a man like him would listen to.

My God. I realised. I just knew. I really hadn't expected . . .

It was him I had got it from. It was him who had made me into me. Well, as much as anyone had. This was home, but it was really none of my business being here. Huh. One last garden-hop. The music tinkled into the woods. My shakes had gone. I knew the journey had ended and it was time to revert to where it had started. I was glad it had ended where it had.

I turned to Stella and said: 'I think we'd better get out of here.'

Postscript

Jill, the girl from Barnardo's, came to see me. She came ten hours on the coach from Devon. Then she came again, when I hadn't asked her, and it all went wrong.

She sent me pictures of graves with my and others' names on them, and 'RIP' pencilled in. Eventually, I had to get the police involved.

Later, she said she was so sorry, she didn't know what had got into her. But it was too late. I don't want to hurt her, however. Tangled flowers.

And Marianne threatened legal action over this book, then withdrew it.

And when I set out I thought it would be such a happy story.

And Mum . . .

Christ, give us a break, will you, girls?

Kate and Andrew are OK. I'm still their leader, I think.

Might even try Brian again. Don't quite know what his problem is.

I would respond, in his position.

Took my daughters to see the Moscow City Ballet on tour. They were rapt. Scared they wouldn't be. Beautiful. Must be something in the genes, somehow.

And just now I was coming out of Riley's snooker club with Georgie-boy. He had just won the world-championship series against me, 10–9.

As we walked across the car park he said, 'Dad, I know I won, but I didn't play as well as I could have.'

'No, maybe you didn't, kiddo,' I said. 'And you know why?'

'Why, Dad?' he said.

'Because when the table next to ours got lit up and they started playing, it spooked you and put you off.'

'That's true, actually,' Georgie said.

Suddenly I was thinking about garden-hopping. Those tables can look like gardens laid out. But my garden-hopping days are finally over.

'Listen, kid-face,' I told him. 'Don't worry about the next table. Play your own game. It's not worth the worry.'